LECTIN COOKBOOK

Discover the Best Lectin-free Slow Cooker and Crockpot Recipes to Reduce Inflammation for Better Health and Vitality

Lactin S. Campbell and Virginia Davis

Fred Ellgen
Pamela Michael

LECTIN-FREE COOKBOOK

Table of Contents

Introduction

Imagine how it would feel finally being free of pain, being free of inflammation, and being free of many of the ailments and diseases that you suffer from each day. Maybe you have tried a wide variety of medications to help. Maybe you have tried every holistic approach, but nothing seems to work.

The solution that you need may be as simple as changing up the diet that you follow. By changing up the diet so it doesn't include foods that are high in lectin, you can reduce inflammation and other issues in your body. This guidebook will help you get started by looking at what lectin is, why it is such a bad thing, and some of the foods that you can avoid to ensure lectin doesn't cause any more problems for you.

In addition to learning a bit about lectin and some of the benefits of following this kind of diet plan, we will also look at some of the recipes you can add to your life to keep you happy and healthy. Reducing lectin doesn't have to be a chore, but you will be amazed by the difference you see once you start, and this guidebook is the tool you need to get that done.

When you are ready to finally get rid of some of the pain and intestinal problems you are dealing with and you want a safe and effective solution, then make sure to read through this guidebook to help you get started

PART 1

Chapter 1: What is the Lectin-free Diet?

The lectin-free diet is one that asks the follower to try and eliminate all, or the majority, of the lectins that they consume in their meals. Basically, the lectins are a type of protein that will bind carbs together in the body. They will then stick to the membranes of your cells inside your stomach, causing issues with your digestion and how well it can work. It can even affect how well you feel each day.

These lectins are going to be found in many foods you eat, including plant and animal products. However, they are found in the highest amounts in legumes, nightshade vegetables, dairy products, and even grains. Some are toxic, such as ricin, and others are not considered as bad for your health. Even the non-toxic ones are able to cause some issues to your health and well-being though.

The point of the lectin-free diet is to help you learn more about lectins so you can understand why they are so bad and you can choose to limit them in your diet. The lectin-free diet helps you to reduce foods that are high in lectins from your diet, including some of your favorites, in order to help you feel healthier overall. It isn't as restrictive as some diet plans and you will still have many options to choose from with this eating plan, but you will need to cut out a few things.

You will find that there is a good deal of benefits that come from this diet plan. It is known to help your digestion, it can clear up health issues like irritable bowel syndrome, and it can even help you lose weight if you combine it with a low-calorie diet as well. Lack of energy, brain fog, extra inflammation throughout the body, and more can also be helped when you go on a lectin-free diet plan.

Where are lectins found?

Lectins can be found in many of the foods that you enjoy today. They are found in higher amounts in foods like grains and raw legumes. Many people who deal with issues from inflammation will choose to cut out lectins, which means they are going to need to avoid foods like grains, anything that has gluten in it, legumes, peanuts, and even some vegetables to get relief.

Why are lectins bad for me?

Humans can run into trouble digesting most lectins. In fact, these can be resistant to the enzymes in the stomach, and the lectins can make it all the way through the stomach without any changes. In addition, lectins can be very sticky and this makes them more prone to attaching to the walls of your intestines. Once the lectins reach the intestines, they are able to disrupt the routine maintenance of the cells, so the wear and tear that naturally occurs there is just going to get worse.

This is the main reason why consuming a large number of lectins in your diet can end up causing issues like digestive distress. Repeated exposure to lectins can end up causing damage to the wall of your stomach. Substances that are unwanted can find their way through the wall and then enter into the bloodstream in a process that is known as leaky gut.

When the lectins begin to leak into the bloodstream, they can interact with various things, including the antibodies. These antibodies are the core component of your immune system, and it won't take long until you have an immune reaction against the lectins, as well as against any tissues in the body that the lectins may have bound themselves too.

There are a lot of negatives that come with eating too many lectins in your diet. While having a few on occasion isn't that big of a deal, some of the negatives that you should watch out for will include:

- Lectins are hard for the stomach to digest.
- These lectins have the ability to cause some damage to the wall of your stomach and intestines, which can lead to leaky gut syndrome.
- These lectins are known to act like an anti-nutrient.
- These lectins are going to interfere with your digestion and how well you are able to absorb foods.
- If these lectin levels get too high, you could run into issues with nutritional deficiencies.
- While more information is needed, it is believed that these lectins could be responsible for several different autoimmune conditions including rheumatoid arthritis.
- These lectins have the ability to upset your digestion, which could lead to lectin poisoning as well as gastroenteritis.

Because of these reasons and more, it is often recommended that people stay away from foods that have a high amount of lectin. And if you suffer from some autoimmune diseases, irritable bowel syndrome, and other issues with your stomach or intestines, it may be worth your time to look at a lectin-free diet and see if it can provide you some relief.

There are some benefits that come with consuming lectins, such as helping with the immune and helping regulate cell adhesion, but this is only when you eat them in smaller amounts. Considering many of the foods that are high in lectin are common in the American diet and are eaten in high amounts, many of these benefits are counteracted and reduced. It is often better to reduce the number of lectins that are consumed to help get the intestines and the stomach happy.

Top Foods that have Lectin in Them

There are a lot of foods that contain lectin in them. Many of these foods are considered nutritious so you may already be consuming them without realizing that you are causing harm to the gut. Although you are able to find some lectins in many of the foods that you eat, some of the places where lectin content seems to be really high include:

- Peanuts
- Tomatoes
- Peas
- Red kidney beans
- Wheat germ
- Peppers
- Lentils
- Soybeans
- Eggplant
- Potatoes

It is important that when you go on the lectin-free diet, you learn how to avoid these types of foods as much as possible. They are going to increase the amount of lectin that is found in your body and can make the health conditions worse than before.

Can I reduce the number of lectins in my diet?

It is pretty easy to reduce the number of lectins in your diet if you know the basics and you take the right precautions. Eliminating foods that have high levels of lectin in them can be the first step. Cooking your food can help to get rid of a lot of lectins, such as in the case of soybeans and other legumes. Soaking and fermenting can help aid this as well.

Reducing the number of lectins in your diet can make a big difference in how healthy you feel and it can be as easy as cutting out a few types of foods and cooking any that you do decide to add into your diet. Fermenting some of your foods can be a unique way to change up some of the meals that you enjoy while still getting rid of those harmful lectins before they can cause more damage to your intestines and cause an autoimmune response in your body.

What are the benefits of a lectin-free diet?

Lectins are in many of the foods that we eat, but many times, we don't even realize we are sick. We have gotten so used to the way that we feel that it seems normal. When you go on the lectin-free diet, it won't take long until you start to notice a big difference. Some of the health benefits that you will notice with this kind of diet plan include:

- Helps fight off sensitivities to some foods

- Helps you to avoid toxic foods

- Can protect the digestive tract

- In some people, it will reduce the number and the risk for ulcers.

- Can assist in losing weight

- Reduces brain fog

Is cooking important on this diet?

Yes, cooking your food is very important when it comes to the lectin-free diet. You should not eat many foods raw, except maybe a few fresh fruits and vegetables. Many of the food products that you consume on a regular basis will contain at least a small amount of lectin. But when you choose to cook up these foods, you are able to eliminate most, if not all, of the lectin that is found inside of those foods.

This is great news for those who are taking a look at the food list for the lectin diet and feel worried about what they will to eat. You will be able to add a lot of these foods back onto your diet, at least in small amounts, when you make sure to cook them properly. And if you are just looking to reduce the lectins you consume, then cooking is going to be your best friend to get that number as low as possible.

There are a lot of different cooking methods that work in order to help you stick with the lectin-free diet. Many people like to work with the pressure cooker because it uses really high temperatures and pressure to cook the food you want to eat. And with those high temperatures, it is easier to reduce the amount of lectin that is found in your food.

Chapter 2: What Should I Eat on a Lectin-Free Diet?

When you are on a lectin-free diet, you need to make sure that you are careful with the foods you eat. You will need to eliminate some of the foods that you enjoyed before to make sure that you limit your lectin intake as much as possible. This chapter will explore some of the foods that you can eat, and some of the ones you should avoid when you are ready to start out on the lectin-free diet plan.

Foods That You Should Avoid

To keep things simple, you want to avoid any foods that contain high amounts of lectin in them. This helps you to avoid inflammation, autoimmune responses, and issues with leaky gut. We will split up our foods into two groups. The first one is going to be foods that you can have, but it is best to limit them as much as you can. They aren't the worst, but eating them in really high amounts, or if you are really sensitive to lectins, can make the matter worse.

The second list includes foods that you should avoid at all costs. It is best to never eat these when you are on a lectin-free diet or limit them to once or twice a year at most. These have really high levels of lectin in them that can make you sick.

The first group of foods, the ones that you should try to limit in your diet, includes:

- Grains. If you do decide to go with grains or products that are made out of grains, go with white flour rather than with wheat.

- Fruit. You can have some in-season fruit as long as you keep the consumption down to a minimum.

- Be careful with the nightshade vegetables. This includes options like tomatoes, potatoes, peppers, and eggplants. You can enjoy tomatoes on occasion as long as they are cooked properly.

- Squash

- Be careful of the legumes. This includes the peanuts, lentils, peas, and beans. You can add these a bit to the diet, but do not rely on soaking them before eating. Make sure they are all cooked properly to avoid as many lectins as possible.

Then, you will also need to watch for the second group of foods. These are foods that you must avoid completely on this kind of diet because they have a ton of lectin and can pretty much ruin all the progress you are trying to make. Some of the foods that you must avoid on a lectin-free diet include:

- A1 Milk

- Any meat that comes from an animal that was corn-fed. You can still eat meat, but make sure that they are pasture-raised rather than ones that are corn-fed.

- Corn

These foods can be really bad for your health and will often cause complications like what we have talked about before. Eating them can cause lectins to build up in your system. While some of them are a bit lower in lectins than other foods, it is still important that you avoid them as much as possible for the health of your stomach.

Foods That You Can Enjoy On A Lectin-Free Diet

Now that we have taken a look at some of the foods that you need to avoid because they are high in lectin content, it is time to look at some of the foods that you don't need to avoid on this diet plan. There are lots of health and delicious foods that you can enjoy because they don't contain a lot of lectin in them. Eating a diet that is full of variety and lots of healthy and wholesome foods can be your best bet on this eating plan. Some of the foods that you can enjoy will include the following:

- Fruits in small amounts: Pick out options that are in season to avoid lectins as much as possible. These do contain some lectins so you may need to limit them a bit.
- Meats: As long as the meat is pasture-raised, it is fine to enjoy it. Go for some healthy options like beef, turkey, and chicken.
- A2 milk
- Sweet potatoes can be consumed, but take the time to cook them first.
- Leafy and green vegetables
- All cruciferous vegetables. These are broccoli, sprouts, and more.
- Asparagus

- Garlic
- Onion
- Celery
- Mushrooms
- Avocado
- Olive oil
- Olives

The foods on this list can be enjoyed as much as you want with your meals. They will provide you with lots of energy and even the nutrients your body needs to heal after too many lectins. Try to fill your plate with as much variety as you can to ensure you get the most nutrition possible. You can also occasionally pair them up with some of the not allowed foods to add in a bit more variety when needed.

When you first get started on this diet plan, take the time to write down this list and take it to the grocery store with you. Then, when you are uncertain about whether a food fits in with this new diet plan or not, you can pull out this list and double check. You can also do the same thing when you are looking for new recipes to try. Even if the recipe is not in a lectin-free cookbook, you can look over the list and see if one of your old favorites will fit in.

Luckily, this guidebook will contain a ton of great recipes that will work on the lectin-free diet, so you are able to get healthy, without having to do all the work.

Chapter 3: Exercising and the Lectin-free diet

While you are on the lectin-free diet, it is a good idea to include some exercise. This can help you to burn more calories to lose weight, can make you feel good, and can speed up the recovery process. If you have never done much exercise, it is important to start out slowly. But over time, you can increase the exercise and see even better results.

There are many different types of workouts that you can choose to do when you go on a lectin-free diet. Mixing the different workouts together can ensure that you get the most health benefits, but remember that a workout you will stick with for the long term is always the best option. Some of the choices that you can make when it comes to the type of exercise you want to do include the following:

Cardio

Cardio is a great option to go with when you want to burn calories quickly and get that heart working a bit better. It is a very effective way to lean up and lose weight and there are a lot of options with this. You can choose to do walking or running, swimming, dancing, biking, and more to help you get the benefits from cardio exercise.

It is a good idea to spend at least a few days a week getting some form of cardio exercise and you can mix up the workouts to ensure that you get something new each day and you don't start to feel bored.

Another option to try out is HIIT. This is high-intensity interval training. You will do your workout at a regular intensity that you are used to. Then throughout the workout, you will add in short bursts, usually between twenty to thirty seconds, of higher intensity. So, if you are walking, you would do a fast pace and then do a full out sprint for twenty to thirty seconds a few times through the workout. This can make the workout more efficient and can help you to gain more endurance while getting your workout done in less time than before.

Weightlifting

If you go on the lectin-free diet in the hopes of losing weight, then you may want to include a few days of weight lifting into your schedule. Many people are scared of starting a strength training program because they don't want to gain bulky muscles or they think it is too hard. But just adding a few weights to your week, you can get lean muscles without to much work.

Start out slowly when you do a weight training program. Just do what you are comfortable with and slowly build up to more. Some workout programs will allow you to combine together your weight training with some cardio and those can be great options as well.

Stretching and Flexibility

It is a good idea to spend a little bit of time doing some stretching and flexibility during the week. You can consider doing a few minutes each day if you would like or do some longer sessions once or twice a week. This could include just some basic stretching or some yoga to help reduce stress and relax the whole body.

These stretching exercises can be nice because they give you a break from some of the other workouts that you do. They are also good for reducing the amount of stress your muscles and joints feel and can prevent injuries when you do the other exercises so you can stay safe and feel great.

Mixing up these workouts can be a great option to help you get all the benefits possible. But if you prefer one type of workout over another, it is fine to spend some time working on that one. It is always better to do that workout if you stick with it than to not do any workout at all.

Chapter 4: Tips to Make the Lectin-Free Diet Easier

A lectin-free diet is not one that is supposed to be really difficult for you to follow. Yes, you will need to make some changes in what you eat on a daily basis, but it can be really effective at helping you with a bunch of health conditions and helping you to feel better. But there may be times when you want to indulge or you feel it is too hard to stick on this diet plan. Some of the tips that you can follow to make the lectin-free.diet easier include:

- Use a pressure cooker: The high temperatures that are in a pressure cooker can be great for reducing lectin levels in food, plus it helps you to get meals done quickly.

- Eat some extra fiber: Since you are cutting out some vegetables and legumes, it can be a bit more difficult to get enough fiber into your diet. Consider adding in a dietary supplement to help you get enough fiber. Or eat enough vegetables and fruits to help you get the fiber that you need.

- Find someone to do the diet with you: Going on a diet plan alone can be hard. If you can find someone else to do it with you, you will have someone to support you, someone to be on your side, and someone there to encourage you along the way.

- Take out one food at a time: If you are worried about getting started on the lectin-free diet, you may want to consider taking one food from the list out of your diet at a time. This can still get you to the same end result, even if it takes longer, and can make it a bit easier for you to accomplish.

- See what works the best for you. Some people find that they are really sensitive to foods that have lectin in them. If this is true to you, then it is best to just reduce all the lectin-containing products that you have. But for others, you may want to experiment with just taking out one food at a time and see what works the best with you.

The lectin diet can be a great option to help you to get rid of some common health concerns simply by taking a few types of foods out of your diet. By following some of the tips above, you will be able to get the most benefits out of this diet plan without any trouble at all!

Chapter 5: Lectin-Free Diet Breakfast Delights

Nutty Oatmeal

What's inside:

- Blueberries (.5 c.)
- Ground nutmeg (.25 tsp.)
- Cinnamon (1 tsp.)
- Diced avocado (1)
- Stevia (2 Tbsp.)
- Sliced almonds (.5 c.)
- Chopped pecans (.5 c.)
- Shredded coconut (1 c.)
- Coconut milk (1 c.)
- Coconut oil (1 Tbsp.)

How to make:

1. Take out the inner pot of the slow cooker and grease it with some coconut oil. Place it back inside.
2. Add in the nutmeg, cinnamon, stevia, avocado, almonds, pecans, coconut, and coconut milk to the slow cooker.
3. Add the lid to the top and cook on a low setting for eight hours.
4. Top the oatmeal with some blueberries and then enjoy.

Sausage Meatloaf

What's inside:

- Mashed banana (1 c.)
- Salt (.5 tsp.)
- Pepper
- Fennel seeds (1 tsp.)
- Dried thyme (1 tsp.)
- Dried oregano (2 tsp.)
- Garlic, minced (2 tsp.)
- Almond flour (.5 c.)
- Chopped sweet onion (1)
- Ground pork (2 lbs.)
- Olive oil (1 Tbsp.)

How to make:

1. Use some olive oil to grease the inside of the slow cooker.
2. Bring out a bowl and mix together the salt, pepper, fennel seeds, thyme, garlic, oregano, almond flour, banana, onion, and pork.
3. Pour this mixture into the slow cooker and form it into a loaf. Make sure there is about half an inch on all sides of the meat.
4. Place the lid on top of this mixture and cover it up. Cook on a low setting until the meat is cooked through.
5. After this time, slice up the meatloaf before serving.

Creamy Broccoli Casserole

What's inside:

- Cashew cream (1.5 c.)
- Pepper
- Ground nutmeg (.5 tsp.)
- Coconut milk (2 c.)
- Almond flour (.25 c.)
- Cauliflower (1 lb.)
- Broccoli (1 lb.)
- Olive oil (1 Tbsp.)

How to make:

1. Grease the slow cooker with some olive oil. Then add the prepared cauliflower and broccoli inside.
2. Take out a bowl so that you can stir together a cup of the cashew cream with the pepper, coconut milk, and almond flour.
3. Pour this mixture over the vegetables and then add the rest of the cashew cream on top.
4. Cover up the slow cooker and cook on a low setting for six hours before serving.

Healthy Granola

What's inside:

- Salt (.25 tsp.)
- Nutmeg, ground (.25 tsp.)
- Cinnamon (.5 tsp.)
- Stevia (2 Tbsp.)
- Slivered almonds (.5 c.)
- Hazelnuts (.5 c.)
- Shredded coconut (1 c.)
- Sunflower seeds (1 c.)
- Chopped pecans (1 c.)
- Maple extract (1 tsp.)
- Vanilla (2 tsp.)
- Coconut oil (.5 c.)

How to make:

1. Take out a bowl and combine together the vanilla, maple, and oil. Stir it well before adding in the salt, cinnamon, nutmeg, stevia, almonds, hazelnuts, sunflower seeds, coconut, and pecans.

2. Toss these ingredients together well before moving over to the slow cooker.

3. Add the lid on top and cook these ingredients on a low setting for three hours.

4. Move the granola over to a baking sheet and then cover up with foil. Allow the granola a time to cool down before serving for supper.

Chapter 6: Chicken and Poultry Dishes

Chicken Taco Dish

What's inside:

- Taco seasoning (3 Tbsp.)
- Chicken broth (1 c.)
- Chicken breast (1 lb.)

How to make:

1. Take out a bowl and mix together the broth and the taco seasoning.
2. Prepare the slow cooker and then add the chicken breasts inside. Pour the broth mixture on top of the chicken.
3. Place the lid on top of the chicken and then let it cook on a medium setting for six hours.
4. After this time is up, turn the heat off and let the chicken set for a few minutes. Take the lid off and use a fork to shred the chicken.
5. Serve the chicken with some sweet potatoes and your chosen sauce.

Mushroom and Bacon Chicken

What's inside:

- Coconut cream (1 c.)
- Chopped thyme (2 tsp.)
- Chicken broth (.5 c.)
- Garlic, minced (1 Tbsp.)
- Diced onion (1 sweet)
- Quartered button mushrooms (2 c.)
- Chicken (2 lbs.)
- Diced bacon (.25 lb.)
- Coconut oil (3 Tbsp.)

How to make:

1. Take out a skillet and warm it up on the stove. Add in a few tablespoons of oil and give the oil time to warm up in the skillet.
2. When the oil is warm, add in the bacon and let it cook until it reaches the doneness level that you like. Move the bacon over to a plate and set to the side.
3. Add your chicken to this skillet and let it brown for five minutes. Then move the chicken over to the slow cooker before topping with the thyme, broth, onion, garlic, and mushrooms.
4. Cover up the slow cooker and cook this mixture on a low setting for seven to eight hours.
5. After this time, stir in your coconut cream before serving.

Duck Roast

What's inside:

- Cubed sweet potatoes (1.5 c)
- Chicken broth (1.5 c.)
- Onion (1)
- Duck roast (2 lbs.)
- Dry vegetable soup mix (1 pack)

How to make:

1. Add the duck roast to the inside of the slow cooker.
2. Take out a bowl and blend together the chicken broth and the soup mix.
3. Slice up the onion into quarters and then move those along with the sweet potatoes into the slow cooker, arranging them around the chicken.
4. Pour the soup mix over everything and then place the lid on top of the slow cooker.
5. Cook this mixture on a high setting for two hours. After the time is up, let the meat sit for a bit and then serve warm.

Lettuce Chicken Wraps

What's inside:

- Swiss chard leaves for wraps
- Pepper
- Salt
- Red pepper flakes (.25 tsp.)
- Ground ginger
- Coconut aminos (.33 c)
- Crushed pineapple (8 oz.)
- Minced garlic cloves (3)
- Diced onion (.5)
- Chicken thighs (.5 lbs.)
- Chicken breast (1 lb.)

How to make:

1. Add the garlic, chicken, and onion to the slow cooker.
2. Take out a bowl and combine together the pepper, salt, red pepper flakes, coconut aminos, lime juice, and pineapple.
3. Stir this well and combine to the slow cooker. Stir well and cook on a low setting for about four hours.
4. After this time, take the chicken out and shred it up with a fork. Return the chicken to the slow cooker.
5. Assemble the wraps by laying out the lettuce leaves and adding some of the chicken mixture on top before serving.

Turkey Legs

What's inside:

- Chopped parsley (2 Tbsp.)
- Chicken broth (.5 c.)
- Poultry seasoning (2 tsp.)
- Dried thyme (1 Tbsp.)
- pepper
- salt
- turkey legs (2 lbs.)
- olive oil (3 Tbsp.)

How to make:

1. Take out a skillet and let it warm up with a few tablespoons of olive oil on the stove.
2. Season your turkey with some pepper and salt along with the poultry seasoning and the thyme.
3. Add the turkey to the skillet and let it brown for about seven minutes before transferring over to the slow cooker.
4. Add the broth around the turkey legs and then place the lid on top of the slow cooker.
5. This dish will need to cook for about seven hours on a low setting. Serve this with the parsley and enjoy.

Chapter 7: Seafood Options the Whole Family will Love

Coconut Shrimp

What's inside:

- Cilantro (.25 c.)
- Lemon garlic seasoning (2.5 tsp.)
- Thai Red curry sauce (.5 c.)
- Water (1.75 c.)
- Light coconut milk (3.75 c.)
- Shrimp (1 lb.)

How to make:

1. Take out the slow cooker and add in the cilantro, lemon garlic seasoning, water, red curry sauce, and coconut milk.
2. Give everything a stir before cooking on a high setting for about two hours.
3. After this time, add the shrimp to the mixture and cook for another thirty minutes.
4. Garnish with some cilantro before serving.

Shrimp Scampi

What's inside:

- Raw shrimp (1 lb.)
- Minced parsley (2 tsp.)
- Chopped garlic clove (2 tsp.)
- Olive oil (2 Tbsp.)
- White wine vinegar (.5 c.)
- Fish stock (.25 c.)

How to make:

1. Take out the slow cooker and add in the parsley, chopped garlic, lemon juice, olive oil, white wine vinegar, lemon juice, and fish stock.
2. Add in the thawed shrimp and place the lid on top of the slow cooker.
3. This dish will cook on a low setting for 150 minutes. After the time is up, take the lid off and serve warm.

Asparagus Tilapia Dish

What's inside:

- Clarified butter (.5 Tbsp. for every fillet)
- Lemon juice (12 Tbsp.)
- Pepper
- Tilapia fillets (4 to 6)
- Asparagus (1 bunch)

How to make:

1. Cut out enough foil so that each fillet has a piece. Then divide up the asparagus so there is an even amount to go with each fillet.
2. Lay the fillets on the foil and sprinkle with some lemon juice and pepper. Add the butter to the top.
3. Fold the foil on top of the fish and seal up the ends. Do the same thing with all of the fillets and then add to the slow cooker.
4. Cook this on a high setting for about two hours before serving

Chapter 8: Meat Recipes

Pot Roast

What's inside:

- Pepper
- Salt
- Beef broth (.5 c.)
- Steak seasoning (1 Tbsp.)
- Quartered yellow onion (1)
- Baby carrots (1 lb.)
- Quartered russet potatoes (1 lb.)
- Trimmed chuck roast (2 lbs.)

How to make:

1. Slice up the roast into four pieces. Arrange the beef along with the onion, potatoes, carrot, and beef in the slow cooker.
2. Sprinkle these with the steak seasoning and pour the broth on top.
3. Place the lid on the slow cooker and cook this on a low setting for eight hours.
4. After this time is up, move the beef over to a cutting board and slice up.
5. Serve this with the juice and the veggies in the slow cooker and enjoy!

Beef Brisket

What's inside:

- Garlic powder (1 tsp.)
- Stevia (2 Tbsp.)
- Dijon mustard (2 tsp.)
- Worcestershire sauce (2 Tbsp.)
- Apple cider vinegar (.33 c.)
- Ketchup (.5 c.)
- Pepper
- Salt
- Chili powder (2 tsp.)
- Garlic powder (2 tsp.)
- Trimmed beef brisket (5 lbs.)

How to make:

1. Bring out your slow cooker and place the brisket inside.
2. Take out a bowl and combine together the pepper, chili powder, and garlic powder. Use this mixture to rub the brisket on all sides.
3. In another bowl, combine together the garlic powder, stevia, Dijon mustard, Worcestershire sauce, apple cider vinegar, and ketchup.
4. Pour this sauce over your brisket before adding the lid to the top.
5. Cook this on a low setting for the next ten hours.
6. When the time is up, move the brisket over to a cutting board and slice it into thin pieces.
7. Return the sliced brisket to your slow cooker and stir in with the sauce before serving.

Dijon Pork Chops

What's inside:

- Chopped thyme (1 tsp.)
- Cashew cream (1 c.)
- Pork chops (4)
- Maple extract (1 tsp.)
- Minced garlic (1 tsp.)
- Dijon mustard (.25 c.)
- Chopped onion, sweet (1)
- Chicken broth (1 c.)
- Olive oil (1 Tbsp.)

How to make:

1. Add some olive oil into the slow cooker to grease it up a bit. Then add in the maple extract, Dijon mustard, garlic, onion, and broth.
2. Stir these ingredients together well before adding the pork chops on top.
3. Place the lid on the slow cooker and cook these for eight hours on a low setting.
4. After the eight hours are done, stir in the cashew cream and top with some thyme before serving.

Swiss Steak

What's inside:

- Coconut cream (.33 c.)
- Minced parsley (2 Tbsp.)
- Pepper
- Salt
- Beef blade steaks (6)
- Dried thyme (1 tsp.)
- Sliced white mushrooms (1.5 lbs.)
- Sliced yellow onion (2)
- Chicken broth (.5)

How to make:

1. Prepare the slow cooker and then add in the thyme, mushrooms, onions, and broth.
2. When those ingredients are ready, add the beef to it and season everything with the pepper and salt.
3. Cover the slow cooker and let these ingredients cook on a low setting for the next nine hours.
4. After this time, move the steak to a platter and cover with some foil.
5. Allow the liquid to settle on the bottom of the slow cooker for a bit, and then use a spoon to move the extra fat from the top.
6. Add the parsley and the cream to the slow cooker and season with some pepper and salt.
7. Serve the steaks with some of this sauce when it is ready & enjoy!

Lamb Steaks

What's inside:

- Chopped bell pepper (.25 c.)
- Chopped mint (1 Tbsp.)
- Basil, chopped (1 Tbsp.)
- Chicken broth (.5 c.)
- Lamb steaks (4)
- Pepper
- Salt
- Minced garlic cloves (3)

How to make:

1. To start this recipe, take out a bowl and stir together the pepper, salt, and garlic.
2. Use this mixture to rub the lamb steak on all sides before moving it over to the slow cooker.
3. Pour the broth all over the lamb steaks before adding the lid on top. Cook these for the next five hours on a low heat setting.
4. After that time is done, move the steak to a serving platter and season with some more pepper and salt.
5. Garnish this steak with some bell peppers, mint, and basil before serving.

Chapter 9: Soups and Stews

Turkey and Spinach Soup

What's inside:

- Red chili flakes
- Salt
- Cubed turkey meat (1 c.)
- Minced ginger (1 Tbsp.)
- Oregano (1 Tbsp.)
- Baby spinach (4 c.)

How to make:

1. Take all of the ingredients except the meat and add to the slow cooker.
2. Add in enough water to help cover up the vegetables and then close the lid on the slow cooker.
3. After seven hours on a low heat setting, turn off the heat and let it set for a few minutes.
4. Take the lid off the soup and use an immersion blender to help make the soup smooth.
5. Now, add in the turkey cubes and close the lid. Cook this for another hour on a low setting before stirring and serving.

Sausage Soup

What's inside:

- Mushroom stock (3 c.)
- Red chili flakes
- Salt
- Minced ginger (2 Tbsp.)
- Cubed sausages (1 c.)
- Chopped onion (1 c.)

How to make:

1. Take the mushroom stock, red chili flakes, salt, ginger, sausages, and onion and add them to your slow cooker.
2. Place the lid on top and cook for six hours on a low heat setting.
3. After this time, let the soup set for a bit before opening the lid.
4. Stir everything around well and then cook for another few minutes without the lid on top. Serve it warm.

Feisty Crab Soup

What's inside:

- Salt (1 tsp.)
- Vegetable broth (3 c.)
- Red chili flakes
- Salt
- Minced garlic (1 Tbsp.)
- Cubed crab meat (1 c.)

How to make:

1. Take your crab cubes and coat them with some lime juice. Let them set to the side for a bit.
2. Now, add these along with the rest of the ingredients into the slow cooker and place the lid on top.
3. Cook these on a medium setting for the next three hours.
4. After that time, take the lid off, turn down the heat setting to low, and allow the soup to simmer for a bit longer.
5. Check your seasonings to see if they are enough for you and then serve.

Onion and Garlic Borscht

What's inside:

- Arrowroot (2 Tbsp.)
- Coconut cream (1 c.)
- Dried dill weed (1 tsp.)
- Bay leaf (1)
- Red bell pepper paste (5 Tbsp.)
- Vegetable broth (8 c.)
- Chopped carrots (3)
- Onions and garlic (2 c.)

How to make:

1. Take out the slow cooker and add the dill weed, bay leaf, pepper paste, carrots, vegetable broth, onion, and beets.
2. Cover the slow cooker and cook for six hours on a low heat setting.
3. Take the lid off the slow cooker and discard the bay leaf. Then bring out your immersion blender to puree the soup.
4. Mix a bit of the soup liquid with the coconut cream and arrowroot. Stir this back into the soup.
5. Cover and cook on a low setting for another 20 minutes to get the soup to thicken before ser

PART 2

Chapter 1: What is The Freestyle Way?

As you begin your journey using the Freestyle techniques, you will learn it utilizes the elements of calories in and calories out. The point system assigns specific points based on the nutritional and calorie content. Your activity level also influences how the points are assigned to offset against the food points.

One excellent online resource to discover your points is available at "healthyweightforum.org/eng/calculators/ww-points-allowed/" The information involved includes your gender, age, activity level, weight, height, and how many pounds you want to lose. The math is calculated for you to show how many points you can consume on your meal plan daily.

For example, a 65-year old woman who has a sedentary lifestyle, is 5'1" tall, 174 lbs. who wants to lose 10 pounds is allowed 24 points for the first 2 weeks and 23 points for the next 3 weeks.

All you need to do is add the points for additional optional or toppings that are not included in the recipe. Each food added to the product will possibly raise the content of fat or sugar. Proteins are calculated into the equation to help lower the points.

The goal is to get you on the right track of choosing leaner proteins and eating more fruits and vegetables with each meal. By increasing these food items, you are lowering the unhealthy fats and consuming less sugar. You will be surprised by many of the foods that contain -0- points. It's hard to believe they are diet-friendly foods!

Use your enclosed 21-day plan as a guideline to get your body in tune with the new way of eating healthier. It won't take long before you are inspired. Your family and friends will surely enjoy the tastier techniques used for food preparation. You will also love all of the new zero foods!

Zero Point Fruits

Enjoy most fruits in moderation - only because the calories can add up quickly. The only exceptions to the rule are plantains and avocados. Consider this as you prepare your smoothie, if you add any additional fruits - be sure to consider any possible points involved. This includes frozen or fresh fruit, as well as jarred or canned. Just remember to choose the ones packaged without added sugar.

Zero Point Vegetables

Many veggies are -0- points on the new Freestyle plan. However, as you prepare your meal, be sure to take into accounts the oil and butter used as you make the vegetables. Enjoy canned, fresh or frozen mushy peas, potatoes, parsnips, cassava, yuca, yams, sweet potatoes, and olives - without additional fats, oil, or sugars.

Zero Point Spices & Other Condiments

You can choose from many items including low-sugar condiments and spices. For example, enjoy items such as fresh or rubs, vinegar, broth, dried spices, hot sauce, mustard, salsa, and capers.

Remember, the points consumed will also depend on the amount you are using in your recipe. They may be zero points for a small serving, but collectively, as they are used in the recipe, they may contain more points.

Other Foods To Enjoy Freestyle

- Boneless & skinless chicken breast and turkey

- Ground lean chicken and turkey

- Thinly sliced deli chicken or turkey breast

- All shellfish and fish (excluding smoked or dried fish)

- Canned fish packed in brine or water

- Regular and smoked tofu

- Eggs

- Plain soy yogurt

- Plain Greek yogurt

- Fresh – frozen - canned beans and lentils that are packed without oil or sugar (Ex. Lentils, pinto beans, split peas, chickpeas, black beans, kidney beans, soybeans, and more)

Chapter 2: Breakfast Favorites

No matter what you are craving, just remember, breakfast is considered the most important meal of the day. So, enjoy each one of these selections as you adjust to your new way of meal preparation!

Baked Omelet

Freestyle Points: 2

Yields: 4 Servings

Ingredients:

- Egg whites – 3
- Large eggs - 3
- Greek yogurt - plain fat-free – 2 tbsp.
- Pepper - .25 tsp.
- Salt - .125 tsp.
- Onion - .25 cup
- Bell peppers - .25 cup
- Grated parmesan cheese - .25 cup
- Cubed ham - .5 cup
- Broccoli florets – 1 cup
- Baby spinach leaves – 2 cups
- For the Garnish: Green onion – 1
- Also Needed:
- -10-inch skillet

Preparation Method:

1. Warm up the temperature setting in the oven to 400°F.

2. Chop the veggies. Whip the yogurt, eggs, pepper, and salt until frothy using a hand mixer.

3. Warm up the skillet using the med-high setting and spray with oil to prevent sticking. Add the broccoli, peppers, ham, and onions. Lower the temperature to the medium heat setting. Continue cooking for approximately five minutes.

4. Toss in the spinach and continue cooking until wilted. Blend in the green onions and add the mixed eggs. Sprinkle with the parmesan.

5. Cook 10 minutes on the stovetop. Move it to the oven for 10 to 15 additional minutes until the eggs are done and set.

6. Garnish with a few green onions and parmesan cheese before serving.

Banana Roll-Ups

Freestyle Points:2

Yields: 1 Serving

Ingredients:

- Whole wheat bread – low-cal – 1 slice
- Medium peeled banana - .5 of 1
- Salt-free chunky peanut butter - 1.5 tsp.

Preparation Method:

1. Use a rolling pin or wine bottle as a substitute to flatten the bread.
2. Apply the peanut butter to one side of the bread. Add the banana.
3. Roll it up and slice into 3-4 segments.
4. Enjoy any time.

Broccoli Cheddar Egg Muffins

Freestyle Points: 2

Yields: 6 Servings

Ingredients:

- Egg whites - 4
- Whole eggs- 8
- Dijon mustard -.5 tbsp. - optional
- Broccoli – 2 cups **
- Shredded cheddar cheese - .75 cups
- Pepper and salt – to your liking
- Diced green onions - 2

Use either fresh and steamed or defrosted and frozen broccoli.

Preparation Method:

1. Warm up the oven to 350°F. Prepare 6 muffin tins with paper liners or cooking spray.
2. Whisk all of the eggs, salt, pepper, and mustard. Blend in the green onions, broccoli, and cheese.
3. Divide up the batter and bake for 12-14 minutes.
4. Serve when they are puffy and thoroughly cooked.

Cinnamon-Apple French Toast

Freestyle Points: 4

Yields: 4 Servings

Ingredients:

- Liquid egg whites – 1.33 cups
- 1% milk – 1 cup
- Eggs – 4
- Cinnamon – 2 tsp.
- Apples – 2
- Slices of low-calorie bread – 8
- Also Needed: 9 x 13 casserole dish

Preparation Method:

1. Peel and dice the apples. Grease the baking dish with cooking spray. Prepare the oven temperature to 350°F.
2. Using a microwavable dish to combine and cook the cinnamon and apples for three minutes.
3. Line the baking dish with bread slices and a layer of cooked apples.
4. Whisk the egg whites and milk. Pour over the bread. Bake 45 minutes. Serve and enjoy with your favorite toppings.

Country Cottage Pancakes

Freestyle Points: 3

Yields: 4 Servings

Ingredients:

- Low-fat cottage cheese – 1 cup
- Medium eggs – 8
- Coconut flour – 4 tbsp.
- Bicarb of soda - .5 tsp.
- Almond flour – 4 tbsp.
- Grated zest of lemon – 1 tsp.
- Kosher salt – A pinch
- Vanilla essence - .5 tsp.
- Sweetened almond milk – 4 tbsp.

Preparation Method:

1. In a blender; combine all of the fixings – excluding the almond milk for now. Blitz until smooth.
2. Lightly spritz a skillet with cooking oil spray. Warm it up using medium-high temperature setting.
3. Prepare in four batches – one at a time. Flip only once, when the pancakes start bubbling. Continue cooking and serve immediately.

Egg & Sausage Muffins

Freestyle Points: 1

Yields: 20 Servings

Ingredients:

- Lean turkey breakfast sausage – 1 lb.
- Liquid egg whites – 3 cups
- Minced cloves of garlic - 2
- Green chilis – 4 oz. – 1 can - mild or hot
- Small chopped onion - 1
- Hash browns – 3 cups
- Black pepper – to your liking
- Sea salt – 1.5 tsp.

Preparation Method:

1. Warm up the oven to 375°F. Prepare 20 muffin tins with some cooking spray.
2. Cook the sausage on the stovetop using the med-high heat setting. As it breaks apart, stir in the onions, garlic, and chilies. Remove when the onions have softened.
3. Prepare the same skillet with a spritz of cooking spray. Toss in the hash browns, salt, and pepper the way you like it. Simmer 3-4 minutes. Fold in the eggs and combine well.
4. Dump the prepared batter into the tins. Bake 15-18 minutes. Check the centers for doneness using the toothpick test.

Egg & Veggie Scramble

Freestyle Points: 1

Yields: 6 Servings

Ingredients:

- Extra-virgin olive oil – 1.5 tbsp.
- Diced tomato - 1
- Large eggs - 6
- Baby spinach – 3 cups
- Minced garlic clove - 1
- Red or purple diced onion - .5 of 1
- Black pepper and Kosher salt – 1 tsp. of each
- 2% sharp cheddar cheese - .5 cup

Preparation Method:

1. Whisk the eggs, pepper, and salt.
2. Warm up the olive oil in a skillet. Toss in the spinach, tomato, onions, and garlic. Simmer until done or about 5-7 minutes.
3. Pour in the eggs and simmer 3-4 minutes – stirring occasionally. When set, remove from the burner and add the cheese on top. Serve and enjoy.

Hard-Boiled Eggs in the Instant Pot

Freestyle Points: -0-

Yields: Varies

Ingredients:

- Water – 1 cup
- Eggs - your choice in a single layer

Preparation Method:

1. Measure out the water and add to the pot. Gently add the eggs to the rack basket. Close the lid and set the timer for 3-5 minutes (high-pressure).
2. Natural release the pressure for 5 minutes and quick release the remainder of the built-up steam pressure.
3. Arrange the eggs in a cold-water dish to cool. A few ice cubes will speed the process. Wait 5-10 minutes before peeling.

Muffin Tin Eggs

Freestyle Points: 1

Yields: 6 Servings

Ingredients

- Eggs – 1 dozen
- Fat-free ground turkey breast - .5 lb.
- Diced green bell pepper – 1
- Steak seasoning – ex. Montreal Blend – 1 tsp.
- Red pepper flakes - .25 tsp.
- Black pepper and salt - .5 tsp. each
- Sage - .5 tsp.
- Marjoram - .25 tsp.
- Also Needed: -12-cup muffin tin

Preparation Method:

1. Set the oven temperature to 350°F. Prepare the muffin tin with cooking spray.
2. Spray the skillet and add the turkey, pepper flakes, black pepper, marjoram, salt, and sage. Cook for 7-10 minutes. Stir often to prevent sticking.
3. In a large mixing container, combine the steak seasoning and eggs - mixing well (2-3 min.) until fluffy. Blend in the diced pepper.
4. Once the turkey mixture is done, spoon into the tins and add the egg mixture. Fill about 3/4 full and bake for 30 minutes in the hot oven.

Tropical Breakfast Pie

Freestyle Points: 5

Yields: 4 Servings

Ingredients:

- Refrigerated biscuit dough – 7.5 oz.

- Unsweetened shredded coconut – 2 tbsp.

- Granulated sugar - .5 tsp.

- Fresh pineapple – 1 cup

- Also Needed: 8-inch-square casserole dish

Preparation Method:

1. Warm up the oven in advance to 350°F.
2. Lightly coat the casserole dish with a splash of cooking spray. Break apart the dough into 10 portions and slice into quarters.
3. Load a Ziploc-type bag with the sugar and coconut. Shake well and add the dough bits. Shake gently, but well to coat.
4. Place the biscuits into the dish and garnish with the diced pineapple.
5. Place in the preheated oven. Bake for 25 minutes.

Zucchini Noodles & Poached Eggs – Instant Pot

Freestyle Points: 4

Yields: 3 Servings

Ingredients for the Noodles:

- Olive oil – 1 tsp.
- Large spiralized zucchinis – 2
- Chopped cauliflower – 1 cup
- Garlic cloves – 2
- Small chopped onion – 1
- Large eggs – 2

Ingredients for the Seasoning:

- Ground smoked paprika - .5 tsp.
- Salt – 1 tsp.
- Black pepper - .5 tsp.
- Finely chopped chives – 1 tsp.
- Also Needed: Spiralizer

Preparation Method:

1. Rinse the zucchinis and discard the tips. Spiralize and set aside.
2. Plug in the Instant Pot. Give it a spritz of the olive oil in the stainless-steel insert. Add in the noodles and water and cook for 5 minutes. Set aside and cover.

3. Stir in the chopped cauliflower with a sprinkle of salt. Pour enough water to cover, and secure the top. Set the timer for 5 minutes using the high-pressure setting.

4. Quick release the pressure and add to the food processor with the salt, pepper, paprika, onion, and garlic. Blend until smooth.

5. Return the rest of the fixings into the Instant Pot and stir. Add the eggs on top and saute for around 3 minutes or until the eggs are cooked to your preference. Serve with a sprinkle of chives.

Chapter 3: Lunch favorites

Whether you want some quick chicken, a bowl of soup or a salad; you'll find it here!

CHICKEN

Asian Turkey Stir-Fry

Freestyle Points: 2

Yields: 4 Servings

Ingredients:

- Asian vegetable mix - 16 oz. bag
- Ground turkey - 99% lean - 1 lb.
- Soy sauce – 4 tbsp.
- Minced cloves of garlic – 2
- Minced ginger – 2 tbsp.
- Coconut oil – 1 tbsp.
- Rice vinegar – 2 tbsp.
- Sesame oil – 1 tbsp.

Preparation Method:

1. Warm up the oil using med-high heat. Next, add the turkey, garlic, and ginger.
2. After the turkey is fully cooked; just dump the veggies into the pan. Next, cook it for 4 to 5 minutes or until tender.
3. Pour in the soy sauce and vinegar. Cook for two more minutes. Taste and add seasoning or soy sauce as desired before serving.

Buffalo Chicken Tenders

Freestyle Points: 5

Yields: 6 Servings

Ingredients:

- Chicken breasts – 1 lb.
- Panko breadcrumbs – 1 cup
- Flour - .25 cup
- Eggs – 3
- Red hot sauce - .33 cup
- Brown sugar - .5 cup
- Garlic powder - .5 tsp.
- Water – 3 tbsp.

Preparation Method:

1. Set the oven setting to 425°F.
2. Slice the chicken into strips and pound to 1/2-inch thickness for even cooking and tenderness. Toss into a zipper-type baggie along with the flour. Shake well.
3. Add the breadcrumbs in one dish and the eggs in another.
4. Dredge the chicken in the eggs, then the breadcrumbs. Arrange on a baking sheet and spray with a misting of cooking oil. Bake 20 minutes.
5. Prepare the sauce with the rest of the fixings in a small saucepan.
6. Enjoy the tenders with the sauce and your favorite side of

veggies.

SALADS

Caesar Salad – Instant Pot

Freestyle Points: 5

Yields: 5 Servings

Ingredients:

- Chicken breasts – 1 lb.
- Iceberg lettuce – 1 cup
- Pepper & Salt – to taste

Ingredients for the Dressing:

- Crushed garlic cloves - 2
- Greek yogurt - .25 cup
- Low-fat mayonnaise – 2 tsp.
- White wine vinegar – 1 tbsp.
- Freshly grated Italian Grana Padano cheese – 2 oz.

Preparation Method:

1. Combine the dressing fixings and set to the side.
2. Prepare the Instant Pot insert and spritz with some cooking oil. Warm it up using the saute function. Add the chicken with the pepper and salt. Saute three to four minutes per side. Take it out of the pot and set those aside also.
3. Roughly chop the lettuce and toss in the chicken with a sprinkle

of the dressing.

4. Serve immediately and enjoy.

Ham Salad

Freestyle Points: 2

Yields: 4 Servings

Ingredients:

- Cooked – chopped ham – 1 cup
- Mango chutney – 1 tbsp.
- Onion powder – 2 tsp.
- Light mayonnaise – 2 tbsp.
- Dried mustard – 2 tsp.
- Non-fat plain Greek yogurt – 2 tbsp.

Preparation Method:

1. Pulse the fixings (omit the ham or not) in a processor until smooth.
2. Place the container in the refrigerator for about 30 minutes.
3. Add a dish of cucumber slices for a -0- points.

Pear & Blue Cheese Salad

Freestyle Points: 3

Servings: 4

Ingredients:

- White wine vinegar – 2 tbsp.
- Pear nectar - .25 cup
- Walnut oil – 2 tbsp.
- Ground black pepper - .125 tsp.
- Ground ginger - .125 tsp.
- Medium green pears – sliced - 3
- Torn mesclun greens – 10 cups
- Dijon mustard – 1 tsp.
- Honey – 1 tsp.
- Broken walnuts - .5 cup
- Crumbled blue cheese - .5 cup

Preparation Method:

1. Whisk the walnut oil, nectar, vinegar, honey, pepper, ginger, and mustard until well mixed. Set to the side for now.
2. Combine the rest of the ingredients and add the dressing. Toss well to coat. Chill in the fridge before time to eat.

Tuna Salad with Cranberries – Onion & Celery

Freestyle Points: 3

Yields: 5 Servings

Ingredients for the Seasoning – to taste:

- Red pepper flakes
- Freshly cracked black pepper
- Sea salt

Ingredients for the Tuna Salad:

- White tuna in spring water – 16 oz. can
- Low-fat mayonnaise – 3 tbsp.
- Light sour cream – 3 tbsp.
- Celery - .5 cup
- Red onion - .25 cup
- Dried cranberries - .25 cup
- Lemon juice – 1 tbsp.
- Cored apple - 1

Preparation Method:

1. Drain the tuna, mince the onion, and chop the celery. Core and thinly slice the apples.
2. Squeeze a fresh lemon for fresh juice. Combine the seasonings. Also, combine the salad fixings.
3. When ready to serve, garnish as desired and enjoy.

SOUPS

Beef Chili – Slow-Cooker

Freestyle Points: 4

Yields: 12 Servings

Ingredients:

- Lean ground beef – 1 lb.
- Diced bell peppers - 2
- Minced cloves of garlic
- Cumin – 2 tsp.
- Diced tomatoes – 1 can – 28 oz.
- Green chilis – canned .25 cup
- Kidney beans – 15 oz.
- Onion – 1 chopped
- Chili powder – 2 tbsp.
- Tomato paste – 2 tbsp.
- Salt – to taste

Preparation Method:

1. Warm up a skillet using the med-high temperature setting. Stir in the garlic and beef until browned (10 min. or so). Stir in the peppers and continue cooking 5 more minutes. Sprinkle with the cumin and chili powder.

2. Scoop the meat into the slow cooker with the remainder of the fixings. Stir and close the top. Prepare for eight to ten hours using the low-temperature setting.

3. When done, just taste test and adjust the seasonings to your liking.

Butternut Squash Soup

Freestyle Points: 1

Yields: 8 Servings

Ingredients:

- Raw cubed squash – 12 oz.
- Fat-free vegetable stock – 4 cups
- Green apple - .5 of 1
- Onion - .5 of 1
- Ground ginger – 1 pinch
- Black pepper & Salt – to taste
- Ground nutmeg – 1 pinch

Preparation Method:

1. Warm up a large stockpot and add the apple, onion, squash, and stock. Stir and cover until it boils. Then, reduce the temperature and remove the lid.
2. Continue cooking slowly for 10 minutes and puree with a blender. Give it a shake of salt, pepper, nutmeg, and ginger.
3. Serve and enjoy.

Chicken-Parmesan Soup

Freestyle Points: 3

Yields: 8 Servings

Ingredients:

- Olive oil – 1 tbsp.
- Minced cloves of garlic - 3
- Diced onion - 1
- Crushed tomatoes – 15 oz.
- Chicken stock – 6 cups
- Chicken breasts- no bones or skin – 12 oz.
- Part-skim mozzarella cheese – 1.5 cups
- Grated parmesan – 2 tbsp.
- Salt – 1 tsp.
- Red pepper flakes - .5 tsp.
- Dried parsley – 1 tsp.
- Black pepper - .5 tsp.

Preparation Method:

1. Prepare the stockpot using the med-high setting and add the oil. When warm, toss in the onions. Simmer 6 minutes. Toss in the garlic and continue cooking one additional minute.
2. Stir in the stock and tomatoes. Once it boils; just lower the heat setting. Remove the skin and bones from the chicken and add to the pot with the rest of the ingredients.
3. Simmer until the cheese is melted and serve.

Fish & Shrimp Stew

Freestyle Points: 2

Yields: 6 Servings

Ingredients:

- Minced garlic cloves - 2
- Crushed tomatoes – 28 oz. can
- Diced onion - 1
- Olive oil – 1 tbsp.
- Tomato paste – 3 tbsp.
- Parsley - .66 cup
- Fish stock – 14 oz.
- Clam juice – 8 oz.
- Ghee or butter – 2 tbsp.
- Basil – 5 tsp.
- Oregano - .5 tsp.
- Red pepper flakes - .25 tsp.
- Pepper and salt – to taste
- Raw shrimp – 1 lb.
- Cod – 2-inch pieces – 1.5 lb.

Preparation Method:

1. Use the medium heat setting to heat up the oil in a skillet. Toss in the onion and cook for five to seven minutes. Stir in the pepper

flakes and garlic. Cook for another one to two minutes. Pour in the tomato paste and simmer one additional minute.

2. Stir in the tomatoes, clam juice, and fish stock. Simmer and add the basil, oregano, and butter. Simmer for 10-15 minutes.

3. Taste test and add the cod. Simmer for another 5 minutes and fold in the shrimp.

4. Continue cooking for 4-5 minutes until the shrimp is opaque.

5. Serve and enjoy.

Lentil Soup – Instant Pot

Freestyle Points: 1

Yield: 6 servings

Ingredients:

- Yellow onion - 1
- Carrots - 2
- Celery stalks - 2
- Diced tomatoes with juice – 1 can 15 oz.
- Garlic cloves - 2
- Curry powder – 1 tsp.
- Optional: Cayenne pepper - 1 pinch
- Ground cumin – 1 tsp.
- Dry green or brown lentils – 1 cup
- Water – 3 cups
- Freshly cracked black pepper – to taste
- Salt – 1 tsp. or more
- Fresh spinach - roughly chopped – 1 cup
- For Serving: Lemon slices

Preparation Method:

1. Plug in the Instant Pot to warm up for 10-15 minutes.
2. Peel and chop the onions, celery, and carrots. Mince the cloves of garlic and roughly chop the spinach.

3. Combine in the Instant Pot; the water, lentils, cayenne, curry, cumin, garlic, tomatoes, celery, onions, carrots, and a dash of black pepper. Stir well. (Omit the salt)

4. Close the top and lock it down. Set the timer for 10 minutes using the high-pressure setting. When it's done; just natural release the pressure for about 10 minutes and open the lid.

5. Stir and make sure the soup is well done. Add 1 teaspoon of salt with the spinach.

6. Serve warm after the spinach wilts. Garnish with a lemon wedge. Serve any time for up to a week when stored in the fridge in an air-tight container.

Vegetable Soup

Freestyle Points: -0-

Yields: 6 Servings

Ingredients:

- Minced cloves of garlic - 3
- Chopped onion - 1
- Chicken stock - fat-free – 3 cups
- Frozen spinach – 10 oz.
- Diced zucchini - .5 cup
- Green beans - .5 cup
- Chopped carrots - .5 cup
- Tomato paste – 1 tbsp.
- Salt & Black pepper – to your liking
- Italian seasoning – 1 tsp.

Preparation Method:

1. Lightly spray a saucepan with some cooking oil spray. Warm it up using the medium heat setting and toss in the onion and garlic.
2. Cook about five minutes and stir in the tomato paste, stock, carrots, and green beans. Prepare for about 6 minutes.
3. Fold in the zucchini and simmer 5 additional minutes before adding the spinach to cook until heated.
4. Season to your liking and serve.

Chapter 4: Scrumptious dinner choices: Beef – Fish & Seafood

Dinnertime is a special time of the day where your family can sit down and enjoy the conversations of daily events. From beef to fish and seafood, you will find a tempting dish to fit any occasion.

BEEF CHOICES

Beef & Broccoli Stir-Fry

Freestyle Points: 3

Yields: 4 Servings

Ingredients:

- Lean sirloin beef - .75 lb.
- Table salt - .25 tsp.
- Cornstarch – divided – 2.5 tbsp.
- Canola oil – 2 tsp.
- Broccoli florets - 12 oz. bag – 5 cups
- Chicken broth – reduced-sodium – divided – 1cup
- Minced garlic – 2 tbsp.
- Soy sauce - .25 cup
- Water - .25 cup
- Red pepper flakes - .25 tsp.
- Minced ginger root – 1 tbsp.

Preparation Method:

1. Combine two tablespoons of the cornstarch with the salt and add the beef to coat.

2. Warm up the oil in a wok or deep skillet using the med-hi heat setting.

3. Add the beef and cook for four minutes. Transfer to a bowl.

4. In the same pan, pour one-half cup of the broth and loosen the bits on the bottom. Fold in the broccoli and add one tbsp. of water - if needed. Cook for three minutes with the lid on.

5. Add the garlic, ginger, and pepper flakes. Simmer one more minute.

6. In a mixing cup, combine the rest of the broth, soy sauce, and remainder of the cornstarch. Pour into the pan and lower the temperature setting to med-low. Simmer one more minute and return the juices and beef into the pan. Toss to coat well and serve.

Beef & Mushrooms – Slow Cooker

Freestyle Points: 5

Yields: 6 Servings

Ingredients:

- Lean stewing beef meat – 2 lb.
- Olive oil – 2 tsp.
- Fresh mushrooms – 10 oz.
- Cream of mushroom soup – low-sodium/fat-free – 10.75 oz can
- Soup mix – dry onion – 1 envelope
- Dry red wine - .5 cup
- Suggested Cooker Size: 4-Quarts

Preparation Method:

1. Use the medium heat setting to warm up a skillet.
2. Do the Prep: Cube the stewing beef and slice the mushrooms.
3. Sprinkle the beef with the pepper and salt to your liking. Arrange it in the pan. Layer evenly and brown. Add to the cooker.
4. Brown the mushrooms and toss them into the pot.
5. Stir in the wine and scrape up the browned crunchies. Pour in the soup and soup mix. Mix well and cover.
6. Simmer on low for six to eight hours. Serve when ready.

Jalapeno Popper Burgers

Freestyle Points: 6

Yields: 4 Servings

Ingredients:

- 1 1/3 lb. ground beef – 1.33 lb.
- Finely chopped jalapeno - 1
- Cream cheese - reduced-fat – 2 tbsp.
- Mustard – 2 tsp.
- Worcestershire sauce – 2 tsp.
- Shredded cheddar cheese - .5 cup
- Kosher salt – divided – 5 tsp.

Preparation Method:

1. Combine all of the burger fixings. Divide into six patties and wait about 10 minutes before cooking for the flavors to mix.
2. Grill to your liking (4-6 min. per side suggested). If you prefer, use a skillet and cook for 5-6 minutes for each side.
3. Note: You can also use ground turkey.

Spicy Beef & Zucchini Skillet

Freestyle Points: 6

Yields: 4 Servings

Ingredients:

- Ground beef - lean – 1 lb.
- Olive oil – 1 tsp.
- Minced garlic cloves - 3
- Chopped onion - 1
- Green chilis - 1 can – 4 oz.
- Diced tomatoes - 14 oz. – 2 cans of each
- Drained black beans – 2 cans 14 oz. each
- Lime – juice of 1
- Chili powder – 1 tbsp.
- Chopped zucchinis - 2
- Ground black pepper & Salt – to taste

Preparation Method:

1. Use the med-high setting on the stovetop to heat up the oil.
2. Once it's hot, toss in the onions and garlic. Saute two minutes and add the beef. Once it is browning, stir in the chilis, beans, tomatoes, lime juice, chili powder, pepper, and salt.
3. Continue cooking for 10 minutes. Take off the top and add the chopped zucchini. Cook 10 more minutes and serve.

FISH & SEAFOOD

Apple Trout

Freestyle Points: 3

Yields: 4 Servings

Ingredients:

- Soy sauce – 1 tsp.

- Freshly squeezed lemon juice – 1 tsp.

- Rice vinegar – 1 tsp.

- Granny Smith apple – 1 Medium

- Trout fillets – 7 oz.

Ingredients for the Seasoning Ingredients:

- Black pepper - .5 tsp

- Sea salt - .5 tsp

- Fresh parsley – 1 tbsp.

- Ground dried rosemary - .25 tsp.

Preparation Method:

1. Cut the apple and fillets into bite-sized pieces and squeeze the lemon juice.

2. Whisk the vinegar, lemon juice, soy sauce, rosemary, salt, pepper, and parsley in a mixing dish. Brush the trout.

3. Lightly grease the Instant Pot and add the oil. Using the saute

function, add the apple and fish. Prepare 2 minutes. Add enough water to cover and secure the lid.

4. Set the timer for 2 minutes using the high-pressure setting. When the time is completed, open the lid and vent the steam.

5. Serve with your favorite 'zero' veggie.

Cajun Salmon

Freestyle Points: 1

Yields: 4 Servings

Ingredients:

- Olive oil – 1 tbsp.
- Salmon – 1.33 lb.
- Dried thyme - .25 tsp.
- Salt and Pepper - .5 tsp. each
- Paprika – 2 tsp.
- Onion powder - .5 tsp.
- Cayenne - .125 tsp.
- Garlic powder - .5 tsp.

Preparation Method:

1. Combine the spices to make the seasoning.
2. Brush the salmon with oil and a drizzle of the seasoning.
3. On the Grill: Arrange the salmon, so that the skin is facing downwards. Cook three to four minutes. Turn the salmon over and continue cooking for an additional 1-3 minutes. Choose a delicious side dish and serve.

Chapter 5: Scrumptious dinner choices: Pork & poultry

PORK

Cuban Pork – Instant Pot

Freestyle Points: 5

Yields: 10 Servings

Ingredients:

- Garlic cloves – 6
- Pork shoulder blade roast – boneless – 3 lb.
- Bay leaf – 1
- Kosher salt – 1 tbsp.
- Lime juice - .66 cup
- Grapefruit juice- .66 cup
- Fresh oregano – 5 tbsp.
- Cumin – 5 tbsp.

Ingredients for Serving:

- Salsa
- Lime wedges
- Chopped cilantro
- Hot sauce
- Tortillas

Preparation Method:

1. Chop the meat into four pieces and place in a mixing container.

2. Use a mini food processor and combine both of the juices, garlic, salt, cumin, and oregano. Blend until smooth.

3. Pour the mixture over the shoulder pieces and let it marinate one hour on the countertop. You can also marinate overnight in the refrigerator.

4. When ready to prepare; add the meat to the cooker along with the bay leaf.

5. Cook using the high-pressure setting for 80 minutes. Natural release the pressure.

6. Shred the meat and remove the juices from the Instant Pot/pressure cooker.

7. Pour one cup of the juices and add the meat back into the pot. Season to taste. Keep it warm until serving time.

Pork Chops with Creamy Sauce

Freestyle Points: 5

Yields: 4 Servings

Ingredients:

- Pork loin chops - center-cut – 4 - Approximately 4 oz. ea.
- Non-fat Half-and-Half - .33 cup
- Fat-free chicken stock - .33 cup
- Black pepper - .5 tsp.
- Onion powder - .5 tsp.
- Salt - .5 tsp.
- Dijon mustard – 1.5 tbsp.
- Dried thyme – 1 pinch

Preparation Method:

1. Shake the salt, pepper, and onion powder over the chops.
2. Using the med-high heat setting on the stovetop, prepare a large skillet with cooking spray.
3. Once the pan is hot, add the chops and fry for 3-4 minutes per side. The internal temperature should reach a minimum temperature on a meat thermometer of 145°F.
4. At this point; just place the prepared chops in a closed container and keep them warm.
5. Pour the chicken stock into the skillet and deglaze the browned bits. Stir in the mustard and Half-and-Half.
6. Lower the temperature setting to medium and continue cooking for 7 minutes. When the sauce has thickened, add the thyme.
7. Serve with the sauce and your favorite side dish.

Raspberry Pork Chops in the Crock Pot

Freestyle Points: 8

Yields: 4 servings

Ingredients:

- Boneless pork chops – 4 – 4 oz. each
- Seasonings: Pepper – salt – meat seasoning; ex. Montreal Steak
- Chicken broth - .25 cup
- Raspberry jam - .75 cup
- Balsamic vinegar – 3 tbsp.
- Chopped chipotle pepper in adobo sauce – 1 tsp.
- Suggested Cooker Size: 4-quarts

Preparation Method:

1. Lightly grease the slow cooker. Whisk the finely chopped chipotle, vinegar, broth, and jam.
2. Season the pork chops to your liking and add two of them to the cooker. Add the sauce and the last two chops with the rest of the sauce.
3. Secure the top and cook 4-6 hours on the low setting.
4. Enjoy with a salad or dish of brown rice.

POULTRY

Cheesy Southwestern Chicken – Slow Cooker

Freestyle Points: 1

Yields: 6 Servings

Ingredients:

- Chunky salsa – 16 oz. – 1 jar - divided
- Chicken breast halves - 6
- Corn – 15.5 oz. ea. – 2 cans
- Black beans - 15 oz. – 1 can
- Low-fat shredded Mexican cheese blend – 1 cup
- Optional: Southwest seasoning blend
- Suggested: 5-6-quart slow cooker

Preparation Method:

1. Rinse and drain the corn and black beans. Add to the slow cooker with about half of the salsa.
2. Remove the bones and skin from the chicken. Shake with the salt and pepper or seasoning blend if using.
3. Add the chicken to the pot and the rest of the salsa. Secure the lid and cook on the low-temperature setting until tender (4-6 hrs.).
4. Sprinkle with the cheese. Cover again to melt the cheese (5 min.).

Italian – Balsamic Chicken

Freestyle Points: 1

Yields: 4 Servings

Ingredients:

- Breasts of chicken – 1.33 lb.
- Salt and pepper – 1 tsp. each
- Italian seasoning – 2 tsp.
- Balsamic vinegar – 2.5 tbsp.
- Olive oil – 2 tsp.
- Minced garlic cloves - 3
- Sliced mushrooms - 8 oz.
- Chicken stock - .5 cup

Preparation Method:

1. Combine the salt, pepper, and Italian seasoning. Sprinkle the chicken.

2. Warm up a skillet with the oil using the med-high heat setting. When ready, add the seasoned chicken. Simmer slowly for two to three minutes on each side. Put it to the side for now.

3. Toss the garlic and mushrooms into the pan and saute three to four minutes. Stir in the vinegar and chicken stock. Stir well and deglaze the pan. Toss the chicken in the sauce and simmer about 10 to 15 minutes until done.

4. Note: Be sure to use high-quality balsamic vinegar for the best results.

Oven-Baked Chicken Kebabs – Slow Cooker

Freestyle Points: 2

Yields: 4 Servings

Ingredients:

- Olive oil – 2 tbsp.
- Fresh parsley - .25 cup
- Taco seasoning – 1 tsp.
- Salt – 1 tsp.
- Minced cloves of garlic - 3
- Boneless chicken breasts – 1.33 lb.
- Yellow - red or mixed bell peppers - 2
- Cherry tomatoes – a small handful
- Onion – 1 small
- Juiced limes - 2

Preparation Method:

1. Cut the onion and peppers into chunks. Juice the lime.
2. Add the taco seasoning, salt, garlic, oil, juice of the lime, and parsley in a blender. Process until it's smooth.
3. Cube the chicken and shake in the bag of prepared marinade. Store in the fridge for about 30 minutes.
4. When ready to prepare, warm up the oven broiler.
5. Arrange the chicken tomatoes, peppers, and onions on skewers.
6. Add the prepared kebabs onto a baking tin.

7. Bake for 5 minutes and flip. Broil for another 5 minutes.

8. Serve when the chicken reaches an internal temperature of 165°F.

9. Note: You can add other fixings to the kebabs if you have some extras on hand. (Be sure to check for any additional points.)

Pesto Baked Chicken

Freestyle Points: 3

Yields: 4 Servings

What You Need:

- Butterflied chicken breasts – 1 lb.
- Pesto - .25 cup
- Low-fat grated mozzarella cheese - .5 cup
- Cherry tomatoes- 1 cup
- Sea salt & Freshly cracked black pepper – to your liking

Preparation Method:

1. Cut away all of the bones and skin from the chicken. Slice the tomatoes into halves.
2. Warm up the oven to 400°F. Prepare a baking tin with a sheet of aluminum foil and a spritz of non-stick spray.
3. Coat with the pepper and salt with a spread of the pesto.
4. Place on the baking tin with the tomatoes. Bake 15-17 minutes.
5. Take it out of the oven and drizzle with the cheese. Bake another 5-6 minutes until the cheese is lightly browned.

Chapter 6: Delicious sides

Pair off one of these delicious dishes with your main course.

SIDES

Asparagus Sauteed with Bacon

Freestyle Points: 1

Yields: 4 Servings – .66 cup each

Ingredients:

- Medium sliced shallot - 1
- Asparagus – 1 lb.
- Sea salt - .25 tsp.
- Freshly cracked black pepper - .125 tsp.
- Center-cut bacon – 4 slices
- White wine vinegar – 1.5 tsp.

Preparation Method:

1. Slice the bacon into small pieces. Prepare in a skillet for 5 minutes. Remove and drain on a paper towel. Leave only one teaspoon of grease in the pan and pour the rest in a jar for later or discard.
2. Trim and dice the asparagus into chunks and slice the shallots. Add to the pan and saute about 7 minutes, stirring frequently.
3. Toss the bacon, pepper, and salt over the mixture using the med-high temperature until warm.
4. Transfer to serving dishes and stir in the vinegar.

Brown Sugar Baked Beans – Instant Pot

Freestyle Points: 2

Yield: 8 servings

Ingredients:

- Finely diced yellow onion - 1
- Northern beans -approx. 1.75 cups
- Kidney beans - 1 can – 15.5 oz. - approx. 1.75 cups
- Pinto beans - 1 can or approx. 1.75 cups
- Chili powder - 1 tsp.
- Water - .75 cup
- Ketchup - .5 cup
- Dark brown sugar – not packed - .33 cup
- Yellow mustard – 1 tbsp.

Preparation Method:

1. Rinse and drain the beans. Combine all of the fixings in the Instant Pot. Secure the lid and lock. Use the manual setting on high-pressure for 8 minutes.
2. Natural release the pressure when the time has elapsed (10-15 minutes) or quick release if you are in a hurry. Stir before serving.

Caesar Green Beans

Freestyle Points: 2

Yields: 4 Servings

Ingredients for the Beans:

- Water – 2 cups
- Green beans – 1 lb.
- Low-cal Caesar dressing – 1.5 tbsp.
- Shredded parmesan cheese – 1 tbsp.

Ingredients for the Crumb Topping:

- Powdered garlic – 1 tsp.
- Low-cal butter – 1 tsp.
- Whole grain toast – 1 slice

Preparation Method:

1. Trim the green beans and shred the cheese.
2. Toss the greens into a pot of boiling water. Simmer until tender (5 min.). Add to a colander to remove the liquids.
3. Butter the toast and sprinkle with the garlic. Microwave 10 minutes and add to a food processor. Blitz until crumbly.
4. Serve the beans with a sprinkle of the crumbs and a serving of dressing. Sprinkle with the parmesan and serve.

Creamy Broccoli – Instant Pot

Freestyle Points – 4

Yields: 4 Servings

Ingredients:

- Vegetable stock – 2 cups
- Chopped broccoli – 1 lb.
- Halved brussels sprouts – 1 cup
- Sliced red onion – 1 medium-sized
- Minced cloves of garlic – 2
- Salt - .5 tsp.

Ingredients for the Sauce:

- Soy sauce – 1 tbsp.
- Freshly squeezed lime juice – 1 tsp.
- Heavy cream – 2 tbsp.
- Olive oil – 1 tbsp.
- Ground black pepper & salt - .5 tsp. each
- Freshly ground ginger - .25 tsp.
- Also Needed: Food Processor

Preparation Method:

1. Add the brussels sprouts and broccoli to the stainless-steel insert of the Instant Pot. Pour in the vegetable stock and salt.

2. Close the lid and choose the high-pressure setting for five minutes.

3. When the timer buzzes, quick release the pressure and remove the veggies with a slotted spoon.

4. Prep the food processor by adding the garlic, onions, and each of the sauce fixings. Pulse until the mixture is creamy.

5. Select the saute function and pour the prepared sauce into the insert. Let it simmer for five minutes. Stir occasionally.

6. Serve over the veggies and enjoy!

Mashed Sweet Potatoes

Freestyle Points: 2

Servings: 4

Ingredients:

- Large sweet potatoes - 2
- Salt & Black pepper - .5 tsp of each
- Garlic powder – 1 tsp.
- Plain fat-free Greek yogurt - .5 cup

Preparation Method:

1. Wash, peel, and cube the potatoes. Prepare a pot of boiling water (enough to cover the potatoes). Add the potatoes. Boil using the med-high stovetop setting for 8-10 minutes.
2. Dump the potatoes into a colander to drain and add to a large mixing container. Combine with the seasonings and yogurt.
3. Use a hand mixer or mix by hand to mash the fixings until smooth.

Pinto Beans - Crockpot

Freestyle Points: -0-

Yields: 8 Servings

Ingredients:

- Onion - 1
- Dry pinto beans – 1 lb.
- Bay leaves - 2
- Garlic cloves - 4
- Poblano peppers - 2
- Salt – 1 tsp.
- Cumin - .5 tbsp.
- Water or broth – to cover the beans – 6 cups

Preparation Method:

1. Dice the garlic, peppers, and onion. Rinse the beans thoroughly and add to the crockpot.
2. Toss in the rest of the fixings and cover with broth or water. It should be at least one inch over the beans.
3. Prepare for 8-10 hours using the low setting. Times vary with each cooker. When done, the beans will be soft and tasty.

Rainbow Potato Salad

Freestyle Points: 4

Yields: 6 Servings

Ingredients for the Potatoes:

- Yellow potatoes – 1 lb.
- Purple potatoes- .5 lb.
- Red potatoes- .5 lb.

Ingredients for the Dressing:

- Fresh dill - .5 cup
- Scallions - .5 cup
- Celery – 1 stalk
- Low-calorie ranch dressing - .5 cup
- Salt and pepper – to taste

Preparation Method:

1. Cube the potatoes. Finely chop the scallions and celery. Roughly chop the dill.
2. Add all of the potatoes to a pan full of water. Boil and cover. Continue to cook until softened (10-12 min.).
3. Drain the water out of the potatoes and let cool.
4. Combine the dressing fixings in a mixing container. When cool, add the potatoes and stir until incorporated.
5. Chill in the fridge or serve warm.

Roasted Carrots

Freestyle Points: 2

Yields: 4 Servings

Ingredients:

- Baby carrots - 1 bag – 16 oz.
- Dried parsley - .25 tsp.
- Salt - .25 tsp.
- Black pepper – 1 pinch
- Ginger - .25 tsp.
- Cinnamon – 1 pinch
- Olive oil – 1.5 tbsp.
- Also Needed: 9 x 13 casserole dish

Preparation Method:

1. Warm up the oven to 450°F.
2. Prepare the baking dish with the oil and carrots. Sprinkle with the fixings. Bake for 20-25 minutes until tender.
3. Serve with your favorite main dish.

In the next segment, you will discover how easy it is to prepare a days-worth of meals and stay within your desired goals. Once you know how many points you can add to your menu plan (your personal total of allowed points), feel free to add up to those limits and enjoy the freedom provided by your new way of life. Each day has the total provided for points allowed for each recipe item and a daily total.

Chapter 7: 21-day meal plan

DAY 1:

- Breakfast: Baked Omelet – 2
- Lunch: Fish & Shrimp Stew – 2
- Dinner: Beef & Broccoli Stir-Fry – 3

Totals - Day 1: 7

DAY 2:

- Breakfast: Banana Roll-Ups – 2
- Lunch: Buffalo Chicken Tenders – 5
- Lunch Side: Asparagus Sauteed with Bacon – 1
- Dinner: Apple Trout – 3
- Dinner: Side: Brown Sugar Baked Beans – Instant Pot - 2

Totals – Day 2: 13

DAY 3:

- Breakfast: Broccoli Cheddar Egg Muffins - 2
- Lunch: Caesar Salad – Instant Pot – 5
- Dinner: Cheesy Southwestern Chicken – Slow Cooker -1
- Dinner Side: Rainbow Potato Salad – 4

Totals - Day 3: 12

DAY 4:

- Breakfast: Cinnamon-Apple French Toast – 4
- Lunch: Asian Turkey Stir-Fry - 2
- Dinner: Cuban Pork – Instant Pot – 5
- Dinner Side: Pinto Beans – Crockpot - 0-

Totals - Day 4: 11

DAY 5:

- Breakfast: Country Cottage Pancakes – 3
- Lunch: Ham Salad – 2
- Lunch Side: Caesar Green Beans – 2
- Dinner: Beef & Mushrooms – Slow Cooker – 5
- Dinner Side: Roasted Carrots - 2

Totals - Day 5: 14

DAY 6:

- Breakfast: Egg & Sausage Muffins – 1
- Lunch: Pear & Blue Cheese Salad - 3
- Dinner: Cajun Salmon – 1
- Dinner Side: Fully-Loaded Macaroni & Cheese with Veggies – 6

Totals - Day 6: 11

DAY 7:

- Breakfast: Egg & Veggie Scramble - 1
- Lunch: Butternut Squash Soup – 1
- Dinner: Jalapeno Popper Burgers – 6

Totals - Day 7: 8

DAY 8:

- Breakfast: Hard-Boiled Eggs in the Instant Pot -0-
- Lunch: Beef Chili – Slow-Cooker - 4
- Dinner: Italian – Balsamic Chicken – 1
- Dinner Side: Leftover - Dinner Side: Fully-Loaded Macaroni & Cheese with Veggies – 6

Totals - Day 8: 11

DAY 9:

- Breakfast: Tropical Breakfast Pie – 5
- Lunch: Asian Turkey Stir-Fry - 2
- Dinner: Italian – Balsamic Chicken – 1
- Dinner Side: Mashed Sweet Potatoes - 2

Totals - Day 9: 10

DAY 10:

- Breakfast: Muffin Tin Eggs – 1
- Lunch: Chicken-Parmesan Soup – 3
- Dinner: Spicy Beef & Zucchini Skillet - 6

Totals - Day 10: 10

DAY 11:

- Breakfast: Zucchini Noodles & Poached Eggs - 4
- Lunch: Tuna Salad with Cranberries – Onion & Celery - 3
- Dinner: Pork Chops with Creamy Sauce – 5
- Dinner Side: Roasted Carrots - 2

Totals – Day 11: 14

DAY 12:

- Breakfast: Baked Omelet – 2
- Lunch: Lentil Soup – Instant Pot – 1
- Dinner: Oven-Baked Chicken Kebabs – Slow Cooker – 2
- Dinner Side: Asparagus Sauteed with Bacon - 1

Totals - Day 12: 6

DAY 13:

- Breakfast: Egg & Sausage Muffins – 1
- Lunch: Fish & Shrimp Stew - 2
- Dinner: Pork Chops with Creamy Sauce – 5
- Dinner Side: Mashed Sweet Potatoes - 2

Totals - Day 13: 10

DAY 14:

- Breakfast: Broccoli Cheddar Egg Muffins - 2
- Lunch: Ham Salad - 2
- Dinner: Pesto Baked Chicken – 3
- Dinner Side: Creamy Broccoli – Instant Pot - 4

Totals - Day 14: 11

DAY 15:

- Breakfast: Banana Roll-Ups – 2
- Lunch: Vegetable Soup -0-
- Dinner: Raspberry Pork Chops in the Crock Pot – 8
- Dinner Side: Caesar Green Beans - 2

Totals - Day 15: 12

DAY 16:

- Breakfast: Cinnamon-Apple French Toast – 4
- Lunch: Butternut Squash Soup – 1
- Dinner: Apple Trout – 3
- Dinner Side: Brown Sugar Baked Beans – Instant Pot - 2

Totals - Day 16: 10

DAY 17:

- Breakfast: Muffin Tin Eggs – 1
- Lunch: Tuna Salad with Cranberries – Onion & Celery - 3
- Dinner: Beef & Broccoli Stir-Fry – 3

Totals - Day 17: 7

DAY 18:

- Breakfast: Egg & Veggie Scramble - 1
- Lunch: Buffalo Chicken Tenders - 5
- Dinner: Cuban Pork – Instant Pot – 5

Totals - Day 18: 11

DAY 19:

- Breakfast: Breakfast: Hard-Boiled Eggs in the Instant Pot –0-
- Lunch: Pear & Blue Cheese Salad - 3
- Dinner: Spicy Beef & Zucchini Skillet - 6

Totals - Day 19: 9

DAY 20:

- Breakfast: Tropical Breakfast Pie – 5
- Lunch: Beef Chili – Slow-Cooker - 4
- Dinner: Oven-Baked Chicken Kebabs – Slow Cooker – 2
- Dinner Side: Creamy Broccoli – Instant Pot - 4

Totals - Day 20: 15

DAY 21:

- Breakfast: Country Cottage Pancakes - 3
- Lunch: Caesar Salad – Instant Pot – 5
- Dinner: Cajun Salmon – 1
- Dinner Side: Rainbow Side Salad - 4

Totals - Day 21: 13

Now, just continue with the same pattern and add up to your daily number of Freestyle points. These are just your basic meals; so, enjoy the rest of the points but use them wisely each day.

It is wise to monitor your points closely while adjusting to the diet plan because there is an 'open window' to overeat. Just remember even though you are eating -0- points, they still contain calories that can add up quickly if you eat too many. Thus, you could put on the pounds and not understand why. It is one of the quirks of the plan, but by following guidelines such as the enclosed 21-day plan; you can enjoy many -0- points.

Now, you have the information, it's time to get busy and prepare a healthy meal without the guilt. Enjoy each deliciously prepared meal!

Index for the recipes

As an additional convenience, as you are preparing your menu; you can use this unique index with the Freestyle points listed for each of the recipe selections.

Chapter 2: Breakfast Favorites

Chapter 3: Lunch Favorites

Poultry

Salads

- Caesar Salad – Instant Pot – 5
- Ham Salad - 2
- Pear & Blue Cheese Salad - 3
- Tuna Salad with Cranberries – Onion & Celery - 3

Soups

- Beef Chili – Slow-Cooker - 4
- Butternut Squash Soup – 1
- Chicken-Parmesan Soup – 3
- Fish & Shrimp Stew - 2
- Lentil Soup – Instant Pot – 1
- Vegetable Soup -0-

Chapter 4 Scrumptious Dinner Choices: Beef – Fish & Seafood

Beef Choices

- Beef & Broccoli Stir-Fry – 3
- Beef & Mushrooms – Slow Cooker – 5
- Jalapeno Popper Burgers – 6
- Spicy Beef & Zucchini Skillet - 6

Fish & Seafood

- Apple Trout – 3
- Cajun Salmon - 1

Chapter 5: scrumptious dinner choices: Pork & poultry

Pork

- Cuban Pork – Instant Pot – 5
- Pork Chops with Creamy Sauce – 5
- Raspberry Pork Chops in the Crock Pot - 8

Poultry

- Cheesy Southwestern Chicken – Slow Cooker -1
- Italian – Balsamic Chicken - 1
- Oven-Baked Chicken Kebabs – Slow Cooker - 2
- Pesto Baked Chicken - 3

Chapter 6: Sides

- Asparagus Sauteed with Bacon – 1
- Brown Sugar Baked Beans – Instant Pot - 2
- Caesar Green Beans – 2
- Creamy Broccoli – Instant Pot - 4
- Fully-Loaded Macaroni & Cheese with Veggies – 6
- Mashed Sweet Potatoes – 2
- Pinto Beans – Crockpot - 0-
- Rainbow Potato Salad – 4
- Roasted Carrots - 2

PART 3

Chapter 1: What is the Alkaline Diet?

We eat the foods that we eat for all kinds of different reasons. Sure, from an evolutionary standpoint, we eat food so that we can take in calories and convert them into energy in order to fuel our bodies and keep us going throughout the entire day. The food we eat also provides us with the essential nutrients that our bodies need in order to keep them running in an optimal manner.

But we also eat food for pleasure, the sheer joy of tasting something amazing that we truly love. We eat socially. Food has been a way of bringing people together since the very dawn of civilization. Sometimes we use food for comfort and sometimes we use it to mark formal and important occasions. We use food as a proving ground over which to test out new prospective romantic partners.

And yet, for all that food can do for us, so many of us take it for granted and don't seek out ways to make our food work for us. Used correctly, food and nutrition are tools that can turn our bodies into the healthiest and efficient powerhouse that nature intended them to be.

With so many different diets and nutrition plans out there, it can be hard to know which one is right for you. Well, you're reading this book so you already know that you're on the right track!

Indeed, the alkaline diet is a tried and tested way to get the most out of your body. But how does it work? Why does it work? How can eating an alkaline diet optimize your body and health?

The key to understanding the science and chemistry behind how the foods we eat affect us is to understand that just like the fundamental laws of physics, every action has an equal and opposite reaction. Or in other words, everything that we put into our bodies will affect us based on the characteristics of that particular food item. So if we eat a lot of things that cause the same or similar effects on our bodies, we can influence and even control the effects and changes that our body takes by carefully selecting the foods that we eat and what effect they have on our bodies. As the popular saying goes — you are what you eat.

To illustrate, imagine you are walking through the woods and you accidentally brush up against a poison ivy leaf. Well, sorry to say it, but there is a very good chance that you are going to develop an itchy poison ivy rash. If however, you get completely naked and roll around in an entire patch of poison ivy, you are pretty much guaranteed to get poison ivy and a whole lot of it!

Humorous examples aside, it stands to reason that if we know that a particular food or food group has a particular effect on our body, we can effectively control any number of internal body systems by carefully planning and selecting the foods we eat.

So how does the alkaline diet promote health? Well, the alkaline diet is all about balance. So many of the negative health issues in our lives are the result of an imbalance in our bodies. So much of the history of medicine revolves around finding the ideal balances for the human body.

For many, many years, doctors around the world attributed all of our health conditions, whether good or ill, to a balance or imbalance in what they referred to as the "humors". As far back as Ancient Greece and Ancient Rome, there was a near-universal belief that four humors or bodily fluids influenced every aspect of health and temperament, and ill health or ill temperament was the result of deficiencies or excesses on one or more of these four humors. These four humors were black bile, yellow bile, phlegm, and blood. Each of these four humors was associated with a particular personality type and other such characteristics.

When a person came to an ancient doctor with an ailment, the ancient doctor would examine their patient to determine their temperament and along with other factors would determine where their imbalance in humors was, and then they would come up with a treatment plan with the intention of balancing the patient's humors. So in other words, for millennia, the goal of medicine has been to achieve balance in the human body.

And while many of the theories and practices of ancient physicians have long ago fallen out of use in favor of new techniques and schools of thought, modern science has nevertheless confirmed at least some aspects of ancient medicine, namely, the concept of balance itself.

While we don't hear much about black bile, yellow bile, or phlegm anymore in modern medicine, the fourth humor that ancient doctors treated is certainly still extremely prominent in modern medicine — blood.

Blood is still very much our life force just as it was believed by ancient doctors. Blood is the fluid that keeps us living and breathing and a proper medical understanding is absolutely integral to maintain overall good health.

So how can we maintain a good balance in our blood? What aspect of our blood do we even need to balance? What negative effects can we avoid by maintaining balanced blood and what positive ones can we promote?

While those ancient doctors were certainly on the right track, they had a few key factors wrong so, in order to move forward, we are going to need a firmer and more modern grasp of the science behind our health and nutrition.

To understand this concept a little bit better, we need to understand one of the most fundamental aspects of chemistry. This integral part of chemistry and science as a whole is known as the pH balance or the pH scale. We are going to learn all about the pH balance or the pH scale and how it can affect our bodies in a positive way in the following chapters. First, we will learn what a pH balance is.

Chapter 2: What is a pH Balance?

The first thing we need to understand on our journey to the perfect internal balance via the alkaline diet is exactly just what the pH balance is. Furthermore, we need to understand how the chemical characteristics of a substance or fluid play a role in determining where it falls on the pH scale.

What exactly does the pH scale measure? In short, the pH scale is a measure of the acidity or basicity of solution in which the solvent is water. Such a solution is known as an aqueous solution. In other words, when a substance is dissolved in or is otherwise mixed with water, it can then be tested and measured on the pH scale.

An aqueous solution can be defined as either an acid or a base, as this is precisely what the pH scale is meant to determine. An aqueous solution that is basic is referred to as being alkaline. This gives us a pretty good indication of what the alkaline diet is all about. The pH scale itself is a type of scale known as a logarithmic scale. This means that each equidistant quantified measure is an order of magnitude greater than the previous measurement on the scale. The scale ranges from zero to fourteen, with a neutral pH value being in the middle at seven.

Solutions that have a pH value of less the median value of seven are defined as being acidic, while the opposite scenario, in which a solution is measured to have a pH value of higher than seven — that solution is called basic. Water that is pure and unadulterated is pH neutral which is to say that it should prove to have a pH value of seven when tested, as natural dihydrogen oxide, the chemical name for water is neither a base nor an acid. If that is not the case, then the water should be tested for impurities.

While it is possible for an aqueous solution to have a pH value greater than fourteen or less than zero, these would have to be extremely acidic or extremely basic solutions and would not only be decisively deadly to ingest and even extremely dangerous just to touch. Therefore, for practical purposes, official pH values are nearly always represented on a scale between zero and fourteen.

The pH scale is defined by a set of international standards that are determined and agreed upon by an international scientific body. There are several ways to test the pH level of an aqueous solution, with one of the most notable ones being the use of a glass electrode combined with a pH meter. This scientific instrument determines the difference between a pH electrode and a control electrode in terms of their respective electrical potential. This difference in the electrical potential of a solution relates directly to the acidity of the solution and can therefore be used to give it a standard value.

Another very popular and frequently used means by which to test the pH value of an aqueous solution is by using one of the various compounds known as pH indicators.

A pH indicator is generally some kind of substance that when mixed with an aqueous solution results in a chemical reaction that will literally change the color of the solution, and by examining and comparing the color of the resulting solution, the pH value of the solution can be determined.

There are other pH indicators that indicate the pH level of a solution by chemical reactions that result in other physical indicators such as odor for example. However, by far the most common variety of pH indicators are visual in nature, generally based around color.

One of the most common types of pH indicators is the naturally occurring family of chemical compounds called anthocyanin. These compounds naturally change color reflects the pH balance of whatever item the compound is found within. Generally, these compounds are found in colored plant leaves or other plant parts. One of the most common sources of these pH indicating compounds is from the leaves of a red cabbage. The reason for this is because it is quite easy to extract anthocyanin from a red cabbage making it the perfect resource for a homemade pH indicator test for either health or educational purposes.

Anthocyanin can be found in many different plants though, such as the leaves of the aforementioned red cabbage, but also in certain flowers such as the geranium, the poppy, and also rose petals. Berries and stems can also house anthocyanin compounds such as blueberries and blackcurrants as well as rhubarb. In short, most plants or vegetables that have reddish, purplish, or bluish color in all likelihood contain at least a small amount of anthocyanin compound. When used as a pH indicator by mixing it with an aqueous solution, an anthocyanin compound will become redder the more acidic the solution is and will turn from red to purple to blue the more alkaline the solution is.

Another very commonly used pH indicator since medieval times is the substance called litmus which is derived from various species of lichen.

In fact, the word litmus itself means colored moss in its original language, Old Norse. Just like anthocyanin compounds, litmus will turn red when exposed to acidic solutions and blue when exposed to basic solutions. You may even be familiar with the term 'litmus test'. It has come to be used very commonly and very broadly as a metaphor for anything that could be used to soundly distinguish between multiple options.

So with pH balance being fundamental to the chemical nature of all kinds of biological material including the foods we eat, how do we know if and how such foods are affecting our health? We will continue learning about pH imbalance in our bodies to find out. The next chapter will go into the science of how pH balance or more specifically imbalance can affect our bodies and our health.

Chapter 3: The Science Behind pH Imbalance

Every single substance in the world has a pH balance and that includes all of us. Sure, we don't make cabbages change color when we pick them up, but our bodies must maintain a certain pH level in order to live and function properly. This pH balance that is naturally maintained in our bodies is called the acid-based balance and it is quite literally exactly what it sounds like — the balance of acidic and basic substances in your body. More specifically though, when we are referring to the acid-base balance of our bodies, we are most often referring to the pH balance of our blood.

The human body is designed with a few systems in place intended to keep the natural pH levels regulated at an appropriate balance between acidity and alkalinity. Both the kidneys as well as the lungs have a very important role to play in this process. As we previously laid out, the pH balance is generally expressed as a value between zero and fourteen, with seven being the neutral value. And remember that pure and unadulterated water should have a pH value of exactly seven. Knowing then that water is neutral seven on the pH scale, and knowing also that our bodies are designed to maintain an even pH balance, it would stand to reason that our blood should have a neutral pH value of seven as well, right?

Well, not quite. And this is a major key to understand the alkaline diet. The ideal blood pH level is not actually a neutral seven but instead generally should be about a 7.40 on the pH scale. This value can vary slightly from person to person, but that is the standard average. And yes, that's right— the human body should have a blood pH level that is a little bit on the alkaline side.

Generally speaking, it is the kidneys and lungs that regulate this pH level, so if they are not functioning normally, the blood pH level can become imbalanced. This kind of pH imbalance can lead to serious medical conditions which are called acidosis or alkalosis depending on which direction the imbalance goes in. It is important to note that these serious medical conditions must be treated by a medical professional and diet alone cannot entirely reverse these conditions.

Now, what we're talking about in this book is the small, minor imbalances that a general practitioner wouldn't be concerned about because they aren't severe enough to have a serious debilitating effect, but that certainly do have your body operating in sub-optimal conditions, and more importantly, the alkaline diet that can have it function far better than you ever imagined possible.

So in order to better understand how the alkaline diet will allow us to correct these small but important pH imbalances, we'll need to have a complete understanding of what could throw our pH out of balance and why it might happen.

As we have established a moment ago, the primary regulators of the body's pH level are the kidneys and the lungs. There are a large number of small systems in our bodies that have their own pH level and regulate them in their own ways, but the two main, body-wide regulators are the lungs and kidneys.

As you are likely already aware, we take in oxygen with our lungs when we inhale and expel carbon dioxide when we exhale. The oxygen that we take in is absorbed inside our lungs and used as fuel by our cells. The waste product that our cells produce by using the oxygen is carbon dioxide. Which is all very simple and pretty straightforward and familiar to all of us but here's the important part — carbon dioxide is slightly acidic. So by making slight adjustments to how much carbon dioxide is released or retained, our lungs are able to make adjustments to the overall acid-base level of our blood.

Similarly, the kidneys being the filtration system for the vascular system have the ability to excrete small amounts of acidic or basic compounds into the blood in order to make slight alterations to our blood chemistry. This is a slow process as compared to the more immediate effect of the lungs' pH regulatory system. So the lungs and the kidneys could be thought of as the short-term and long-term blood pH level regulators of our body.

If the blood pH level is out of balance, then it can lead to one of these two conditions — alkalosis and acidosis. With the standard balanced blood pH level being 7.40, anything below 7.35 is considered acidosis and anything above 7.45 is called alkalosis. Again, it is important to note that these are serious medical conditions and must be treated by a medical professional. It is always best to consult your doctor if you are suffering from these conditions. What we can do, however, is assist our body's natural pH regulation system by maintaining a blood pH level that is within the tolerable limits.

A low blood pH level or in other words, slightly acidic blood is far more common than the inverse and so that it is what we are primarily focusing on — an alkaline diet that will help us maintain a healthy blood pH level.

While any level measured at 7.35 and under is acidosis and needs professional medical treatment, it is far too common for our blood pH level to fall into that 'safe' range of 7.36-7.39 without being at that ideal sweet spot of 7.40. If you want to get the most out of your body, if you want your body to be operating at peak performance, and if you want to live your absolute healthiest life, then the 'safe' level of 7.36 is not tolerable for your body.

If you are truly serious about your health and your wellbeing, then the 'safe' blood pH level of 7.39 isn't even good enough for you. You need to have the absolute optimal blood pH level and you will settle for nothing but a perfect 7.40. Continue on reading in the next chapters and we are going to show you how.

Chapter 4: Why Alkaline is Best

If our body's pH level is all about balance, then why would maintaining an alkaline diet be superior to an acidic one? Shouldn't we be consuming a perfect balance of alkaline and acidic foods and nutrition? If those are among the questions you are now asking yourself, then you are on the right track. Those are great questions to ask.

There are several reasons why an alkaline diet is a crucial component in maintaining a healthy body and blood pH level. Remember that magic number? The ideal pH level for our blood that will allow our body to operate optimally? That is right — it was 7.40. And do you remember what the pH value for perfectly pure, unadulterated water is? That is right — it was a perfect seven. So what that means, of course, is that the ideal blood pH balance is in fact slightly alkaline at 0.4 units more basic than water.

So we can see already that in order to maintain our ideal pH balance, we will need to intake more alkaline foods than acidic foods. Of course, that is not to say that you can never consume anything acidic. In fact, it is important to have acids as well in order to maintain balance. We just need to be perfectly aware that our body does in fact require a slight alkaline balance and so we should be mindful of this when we plan our meals and overall diets.

This balance may also be reflected in the foods we choose to eat. They don't necessarily need to be extremely alkaline in order to transfer to us the health benefits we are looking for. They may only need to have a slight pull on the alkaline side of the scale. It all depends on our individual bodies and what they are in need of. And of course, everything scales. So a lot of a slightly alkaline substance may have the same value as a little of something with a higher alkaline value. Remember as well that the pH scale is logarithmic which is to say that each unit is exponential to the value of the previous unit. That means that consuming something with an alkaline value of nine would be ten times more alkaline than something with the alkaline value of eight. This is why we need to be careful when consuming anything that is alkaline or acidic. Things can become unhealthy or even dangerous in a real hurry. So, remember to plan ahead and do everything in moderation.

Another equally surface-level reason why it is important to consume a healthy amount of alkaline rich foods is because whether we are aware of it or not, many if not most of the foods we eat on a regular basis are either slightly or moderately acidic. Some very common foods and beverages even go as far as being highly acidic.

Now, again, it bears repeating that this does not mean that you cannot or should not consume these types of acidic foods and beverages at all. In fact, some of these acidic foods and beverages are very healthy and high in essential nutrients. The important thing, however, is to be aware of how much acidic substances we are consuming and how acidic those substances are.

Do you like fruit juices? How about coffee? Those are two great examples of highly acidic beverages that many of us consume on a regular basis. That is not necessarily a bad thing but just think about this — are you taking in the necessary amount of alkaline foods or liquids in order to maintain a healthy and optimal balance?

And what's more, it can often be a good deal more complicated than whether the particular food item that we are consuming is acidic or alkaline on a surface level. What makes the important difference is how the item we consume affects our blood pH level after it has been metabolized. And that could, in fact, be a good deal different than what it might seem to be based on the original acidity or alkalinity of the food item in question.

Another very important reason to remember to include alkaline foods in our diet in order to maintain a good acid-base blood balance is that an acid rich environment is considered by medical professionals to be a hotbed of disease and illness. And remember, it doesn't take much to become imbalanced in one's blood levels, so even a minor imbalance could quickly become a breeding ground for all manner of illness and health problems that you will absolutely want to avoid.

Just by remembering to consume a healthy and appropriate amount of alkaline foods and drinks, we can be safeguarding ourselves from any number of serious health concerns that could be lurking in our very blood. If you want to kill all of those potential illnesses dead before they become a real concern, you will need to act now and ensure that you are consuming an appropriate amount of alkaline foods.

This is the very topic that we will be going into next. We now know how important it is to maintain a good acid-base blood balance. We now know what that optimal blood pH balance is. And most importantly, we now know the dangers associated with having blood that is too acidic, and why it is so common for us to have a blood pH level that skews a little bit too acidic but not enough to go into full acidosis.

Equipped with this crucial information, we can now move on to learning about how to apply these factors to our everyday lives. Now, we are going to learn everything we need to know about how to create and maintain a balanced blood pH level, and all the tips and tricks to make it easy and straightforward.

Are you ready to have a body operating at optimal health? Are you ready to get the most out of your diet? Are you ready to prevent disease and illness that you didn't even know you were susceptible to?

Then continue on reading on, because all of your questions are about to be answered.

Chapter 5: Creating an Acid-Alkaline Balance

In this chapter, we are going to take a look at some of the biggest and best ways to gain control of your acid-alkaline blood levels and ensure that you can maintain them at an optimal level. Many of the things that we are going to talk about here are not just about diet. In fact, even the alkaline diet is not just about diet — it is about habits. It is about keeping good habits, maintaining regular health goals, and being in tune with your own body.

There are plenty of signs and symptoms that you may notice in the event that your body is too acidic. It is very likely that you will be experiencing chronic fatigue if your body is too acidic. Even if it seems that though you have been sleeping enough, you may still feel this way. Other symptoms of overly acidic blood are pain, headaches, joint pain, and stiffness.

Generally, people with acidic blood express an overall feeling of sluggishness and lethargy — sometimes even depression. It is also associated with a sense of irritability and a dulling of the mental faculties.

Obviously, if you are experiencing any of these symptoms, it will be in your best interest to correct them to the best of your ability. There are lots of ways to make your blood more alkaline and we will look at a few here.

First of all, you will want to make sure that your symptoms or feelings are in fact coming from a pH imbalance. In order to do that, you will need to check your blood pH levels regularly in order to maintain an up-to-date record of your pH levels. You can do this very easily with simple, inexpensive home testing kits available online and at many drug stores. You can get an instant and highly accurate reading and find out exactly where your body's pH balance is sitting. These simple test kits can help you make healthy and informed decisions about your personal health based on accurate and current information. This is a great, convenient, and inexpensive way to always be on top of your health.

Now, before we get into specific diet plans, let us talk about some changes that we can make to our diet in a general sense that will help improve our blood pH levels. One such thing that we can do to ensure that we are maintaining appropriate levels of acidity in our blood is by making sure that we eat more greens and dark-colored vegetables in general. Greens are not always the most popular foods to eat despite their great reputation and association with good health. But there are ways to make greens and other veggies fun and exciting and taste great.

You could try new recipes and try new types of veggies that you have never tried before. If you already love veggies, try to make sure that you get a good amount on a regular basis, if not every day. Even if you have a particular proclivity for veggies, it's easy to leave them out on occasion. Try to avoid that tendency.

And if you don't like veggies, maybe it has something to do with a reduction in their appeal on account of processed foods and excessive artificial sugars. Simply by cutting these things out of our diets as much as possible can dramatically reduce cravings for said items and make good, nutrient-rich foods like dark, green veggies far more appealing.

Either way, try to experiment with new ways of getting your veggies and making them fun and enjoyable. Try keeping some prepared in advance so that you always have a quick and healthy snack.

Here is another quick tip for general health and well-being. Every morning, the first thing you do when you wake up should be to drink a great big glass of ice-cold water as fast as you can. Why? Well, it's quick and it's easy, it costs nothing, and it has all kinds of great health and wellness benefits both short-term and long-term. First of all, the most immediate benefit is that ice-cold blast of invigorating water will snap you wide awake quicker and more effectively than any caffeinated beverage.

What's more, there's nothing better than an icy surprise to jump-start your body and kick your metabolism into a high-gear first thing in the morning. And because our friend water is completely calorie-free, that basically amounts to an energy boost and metabolism enhancer for free, metabolically speaking.

And do you want to take this brilliant life hack one step further and bring it into our alkaline friendly lifestyle? Add just a touch of lemon to that morning burst of water, or better yet, all the water you drink and you will get all the previous benefits plus that boost to your body's alkalinity that you need to function at peak efficiency. This may seem counter-intuitive given that lemon is acidic, but remember, it is not always about the acid-alkaline balance of the compound itself. It is how our bodies metabolize that compound. And lemon, being a well-known metabolism booster, will give you that alkaline push you need.

Of course, sometimes it is about the actual acidity of the food we are eating. Specifically, it is about the amount of acidic foods we are eating. If you find that you are suffering from symptoms of acid reflux, kidney stones, low bone density, or anything else associated with high body acidity levels — that is almost certainly a strong indication that you should be strictly limiting your intake of acidic foods.

This goes of course for any of the obvious culprits like tomato sauce or spicy foods, but there are some less obvious foods that metabolize into an acidic by-product in our bodies that we should be cautious of as well. This includes many processed cakes and cereals, often grain such as rice, oats or pasta, and even certain nuts like peanuts or walnuts. The key here is to just always be aware of what we are consuming and keep everything in moderation.

Beverages as well should be kept in moderation especially coffee and alcohol since both of which are associated with many negative health effects when consumed in excess, far beyond body acid-alkaline balance.

Chapter 6: Alkaline Diet for Vegetarians

Don't let the title fool you, this isn't just for vegetarians. The alkaline diet is great for anyone and everyone. If you are already a vegetarian — great, you are already in a great spot to maintain an amazing alkaline diet. If you're not a vegetarian, that's okay too. Remember in the previous chapter when we said that it is not necessarily about how acidic the foods we eat are but the quantities? Well, that goes for meat. Most meats are extremely acid forming in our bodies.

That means that while they may not be acidic to the taste or even particularly acidic on a pH test, they metabolize in our bodies into an acidic by-product. So naturally, most alkaline diet meal plans are going to be either vegan or vegetarian, or just very light on the meat and dairy. That doesn't mean, of course, that you need to completely remove meat from your diet, but if you choose to continue eating meat, you will need to be highly aware of the quality and quantity of the meat you consume. Keep it moderate and make sure to maintain good health otherwise and you should be okay.

But speaking of acid-forming diets, what so bad about them? We have seen some of the symptoms of having a seriously acidic blood pH level, but what if we're just prone to eating a little bit on the acid-forming side? Well, simply by virtue of the fact that we live in a modern world with modern luxuries and modern conveniences, most of our diets have strayed away from a good, healthy acid-alkaline blood balance, and maybe some of us without even knowing it is may be living with a chronic condition that results from such a diet known as 'chronic low-grade metabolic acidosis'.

This is what happens when our diet leans to the slightly acidic side for an extended, if not an indefinite amount of time. And the reality is that unless we take active steps to counteract this condition, it is highly likely that we will all succumb to it eventually, if not already. That is just the nature of the world we live in and the habits and practices of the industries and populations of our societies.

So if you are suffering from a form of low-grade chronic metabolic acidosis, perhaps without even knowing it, what are the signs? For one thing, you may notice some weight gain. This is a result of inefficient metabolic function on account of long-term low-grade acidosis. You may also suffer from pronounced but unspecific aches and pains. These will often be in the joints or even the bones. This type of pain associated with low-grade acidosis is likely the result of an acid buildup in the joints and bones.

Acid reflux, predictably, is also a good sign of this prevalent condition. But that is not the only part of your digestive system that can be affected. Long-term, low-grade acidosis can also cause a number of other digestive issues like intestinal cramping, irritable bowel, and generally poor digestion.

A whole host of other issues could manifest if you are one of the high percentages of people who unknowingly live day to day with a chronic case of low-level metabolic acidosis. Chronic fatigue and a general feeling of tiredness and muscle weakness may result. As can a number of other issues like skin problems, bone loss, kidney stones, receding gums, and urinary tract problems. So if you find that you have three or more of the many possible symptoms, then at least eighty percent of your caloric intake should be from alkaline-forming foods. The remaining twenty percent can more or less be of your choosing, but you may find high protein food items to be helpful.

A nice, quick and easy way to boost your body's alkalinity is by drinking beverages that are alkalizing. Spring water is one such naturally occurring source of alkalizing water. Also, water with a dash of lemon juice just as mentioned earlier. Green tea or ginger root tea will also have a similarly alkalizing effect.

You'll want to make sure that you are focusing primarily on eating whole foods. So that means vegetables and fruits, as well as root crops like potatoes and turnips. Also nuts and seeds can be an excellent alkalizing source and also a very strong source of protein. Beans are generally a good choice as well, although lentils, in particular, are renowned for their excellent alkalize boost. And when consuming grains, just remember that it is always best to consume whole grains.

Whether you are pursuing an alkaline diet to target a specific issue, or if you just want to have the healthiest body you possibly can, you are going to want to eliminate as much processed and artificial foods as possible. In fact, that goes for everyone, no matter what. Processed and artificial foods are doing anybody any favors, but they will certainly cause your body's blood pH level to lean to the acidic side. Refined sugars and added sugars rank very high up on the list of these types of foods that should be avoided at all cost. And refined white flour isn't doing you any favors either. In fact, some say it can be just as bad as refined sugars.

And while we are on the topic of eliminating things, if you can handle giving up coffee or any other caffeinated beverages, you will be giving yourself a major advantage on the path to a balanced blood pH level.

There are certain foods and nutritional elements that are acid-forming but that our bodies still need to function properly. These are things that we will have to keep a particularly close eye on in order to monitor amounts of intake. This includes essential fats, as well as pasta and other grains. If you are choosing to continue eating meat, then it should also be noted that meat and fish should both be consumed very sparingly and should also be very closely monitored and limited.

Finally, when it comes to dressing up your greens, namely when being consumed as a salad or being cooked, make sure to use high-grade and healthy fats like extra-virgin, cold-pressed olive oil, avocado oil, and coconut oil. All of which bring along tons of health boosts and benefits in addition to their alkaline-forming properties.

Chapter 7: Alkaline Meal Ideas

Now that we are fully informed and equipped to make good nutrition choices in regards to acid-alkaline blood balance, it is now time to put together some meal plans so we can put all of what we have learned into practice. We are going to look at a prime example of everything you might eat in a day to get the most out of your body.

This particular example isn't about limiting calories of eliminating any particular foods or food groups, so if you have any particular calorie counts you need to stay within, or if you are eliminating certain food groups from your diet such as meat or dairy, you may have to adjust accordingly. Just make sure that if you're replacing anything, to replace it with something of a similar acid-alkaline value, and that it serves that same food role as the replaced item. That is to say, replace proteins with proteins, carbs with carbs, et cetera.

And if you are not calorie counting, obviously use your best judgment here but there is no limit to how many alkalizing foods in the fruits and vegetable categories you can eat. Certainly, you should be limiting acidic foods like meats, dairies, grains, and processed foods if for no reason than to keep your acidity levels down, but fruits and vegetables especially the ones that are particularly alkalizing, you can eat to your heart's content.

So with that said, let's take a look at what our alkaline diet morning might look like.

We wake up nice and early in the morning, refreshed and ready to tackle our day because our healthy, alkaline-rich diet is allowing us to get the sleep we need and preventing our bodies from feeling overly fatigued. The first thing we do is get an ice-cold glass of water, squeeze some fresh lemon juice into it and drink the whole thing as fast as we can. As fast as we can without getting a brain freeze that is!

So now we're going to want to have a nice satisfying breakfast. Today, we are going to do a veggie scramble. Sounds great, doesn't it? This breakfast is going to consist of one or two eggs that we are going to scramble up with green onions, spinach or bok choy or any other leafy greens, and then some chopped bell peppers and diced tomatoes. You can even try it as an omelet if you like. Or even an egg-white omelet if you're feeling really healthy.

Or better yet, if you really want to go healthy, why not try that same breakfast, but as a tofu scramble instead of scrambled eggs. It's easy and delicious. Just replace the eggs with a handful of diced, firm tofu. You can season your tofu however you like, but we recommend trying a chili-style seasoning for some nice, tex-mex style breakfast burritos. Wrap optional.

After that amazing breakfast, we're going to have a nice productive and active morning. If we feel the need for a snack before lunch, we'll have maybe a fruit like an apple or a pear, maybe a banana or a handful of nuts or seeds. An ideal choice would be pumpkin seeds or almonds.

If you're anything like us, that already sounds like an amazing and healthy, nutritious day, but we haven't even gotten to lunch yet. So what might we enjoy for our midday meal on this ideal alkaline diet day? Why limit ourselves, let's look at a couple of options.

For one, we could try some lentil soup. This packs a nice alkalizing punch as it is but combine that with some steamed green like broccoli, carrots, onions, or kale, and you've got a powerful meal. Heck, why not steam up a mix of all of those veggies. Try a light olive oil-based salad dressing on the steamed veggies for some extra flavor.

As delicious as that sounds though, we still have another option. If you're still of the animal eating persuasion, you could try a nice big salmon steak, still a far healthier choice that its terrestrial cousin, served with some mixed greens which could include cucumber, carrots, tomatoes, and broccoli, among pretty much any other fresh veggies you would like. Similarly, you can season that with a light vinaigrette of your choice, but we particularly recommend a lemon and dill based one.

After all that amazing nutrition, you must be ready for a snack! Fight off that mid-afternoon slump with a nice alkalizing snack. This one you can keep nice and simple. Try a simple hard-boiled egg, seasoned with sea salt and fresh ground pepper to taste and a garnish of your choice if you're feeling fancy. Or if you're not inclined toward the animal-based foods, try a straightforward but delicious snack consisting of strips of sweet bell peppers, celery, or carrots, or a mix of all is always an option!

Finally, it's time for dinner and this is where you remaining meat eaters are going to have your way. You can have up to four ounces of your favorite meat, whatever that might be, but we highly recommend that if you must have meat, try to stick to something along the lines of fish, chicken, or other types of light poultry. You can serve this with a side of yam or sweet potatoes, baked or prepared in your favorite way and a nice simple garden salad with mixed greens and a light dressing of your choice.

Or for the plant-based folks, you can indulge in some pasta, but try to find or make pasta made from rice or quinoa, or other grains than wheat. Then you can top your pasta with all kinds of delicious veggies like broccoli, zucchini, and garlic. And then garnish with some olive oil and salt and pepper. Now you've had yourself a fresh and healthy food day!

Conclusion

The next step is to put everything that you have learned in this book into practice. Learning more about your body and how it works is always a great place to start and in this book, we learned all about the acid-alkaline balance in our bodies, how the chemistry works, and what are the effects this balance or imbalance can have on our health.

We learned about some of the cutting edge science behind our understanding of pH levels in our body, and how we can fine tune them to the perfect level through our diet and other important practices. The human body is a very complicated and delicate machine, but the more we come to understand it, the better off we are and the more educated we can be in our choices regarding our health and wellbeing.

Now, it's up to you to take what you have learned in the preceding chapters and apply them into your life. Do you have what it takes to be in full control of your own health and get the very most out of your body? Will you settle for a body that works within tolerable levels, or do you want to maintain peak balance in your life and in your health? Then now is the time to apply all that you have learned and prove it for yourself!

CPSIA information can be obtained
at www.ICGtesting.com
Printed in the USA
LVHW081803280421
685864LV00014B/2348